The Native Pony Stallion

A guide to caring for and working with a pony stallion

Caroline Brett

Published by Wildeye

email: info@wildeye.co.uk
web: www.wildeye.co.uk/publishing

ISBN 978-1-905843-05-3

Printed and bound by
Berforts Information Press, GB

Paper used by Berforts Information Press is a natural, recycled product made from wood grown in sustainable forests. The manufacturing process conforms to the environmental regulations of the country of origin.

Special Thanks to:
Sally Leslie Melville, Alan Miller and Piers Warren

Cover photo: Highland stallion, Marnoch of Millfield

Contents

Forglen Highland stallion and colts

Preface

The Native Pony Stallion is designed to give guidance on how to start, continue caring for, and work with an entire male pony. While reference in this book is made to British Native Mountain and Moorland breeds, these recommendations apply to many other types and breeds of pony colts and stallions. This book is not a detailed manual on how to break and train a young horse or pony. There are many excellent books that give specific guidance from foal, to starting a youngster on the ground and through to riding to a high standard. Basic training is the same for all ponies whatever their sex but colts and stallions can have their own idiosyncrasies.

Why Have A Stallion?

Owning a stallion was seen in the past as predominantly a job for men and professional studs. Times have changed. Today an increasing number of small breeders and female handlers now also enjoy the thrill of working with a stallion. Deciding to care for an entire pony is a serious undertaking and should not be taken lightly. Keeping a sweet, homebred colt on the off chance that he might make a nice stallion isn't the best reason for not gelding him. Owning a stallion requires a lot of forethought, time and commitment. While it can be easier to keep a native pony stallion than a spirited, large horse, he cannot be treated just like a mare or gelding. Many stallions need more time and understanding. They need sound, safe facilities and experienced, sympathetic and confident handlers. Holidays, even weekends away, need extra forethought. Stallions need to be supervised by an experienced person at all times, even if only in case of mishap. People often say that visitors wouldn't know that their native pony is a stallion but it needs to be borne in mind that stallions are breeding animals. Their purpose in life is to find a mare, mate and fend off competitors. This fact should not be forgotten. Unless they are going to be used for breeding and/or showing, most colts are better off as geldings. Then they can hack out, compete and live happily with other ponies.

Connemara gelding,
Carraun Lord Arthur

Which Stallion?

If you are undeterred and determined to have a stallion, the next consideration is which one. A showing or breeding stallion must be the crème de la crème of his kind. Stallions can be more 'showy' than mares and geldings and can excel in the ring but only if they are supreme examples of their breed. Judges are unforgiving of faults on an entire pony that is likely to pass on defects to the next generation. A champion stallion though is a great advert for the breed, an asset to the breeder and rewarding for all those involved with him.

All breeders strive to produce the best possible foals not only for themselves but also for the future of the breed. Potential owners should know their chosen mountain and moorland pony well and be familiar with breed standards. All British native ponies are represented by a breed society. Contacting the relevant society for information and guidance is a good way to start. When choosing a stud pony also evaluate potential foundation mares. Most ponies have good and not so good points so choosing a stallion to improve the qualities of the mares he is destined to breed with is a prudent consideration. A quality stallion can only compliment a class mare. Attending native pony shows, mountain and moorland classes and studs is an excellent way of 'getting your eye in'. It's essential to research a potential colt's family history and study his bloodlines. His parents' and siblings' showing records can provide valuable information.

A good stallion can be any colour permitted by the relevant native pony society but some breeders have preferences. Producing a favoured coat colour or four white socks is an inexact science but chances can be enhanced. Crossing a chestnut mare with a chestnut stallion, for example, will only produce a chestnut foal. To have any chance of producing a grey foal you need at least one grey parent. Selecting a stallion that has never sired anything but grey or coloured offspring will also increase the odds. Breeders of palominos use cremellos, chestnuts and palominos to perpetuate their lines. If colour is a consideration, new breeders need to get advice on genetics to understand the role of genes including recessive and dominant characteristics.

Many breeders produce foals with a particular purpose in mind. Dressage enthusiasts have an eye on more exaggerated movement, natural balance, and conformation to enable collection. Those hoping for future working hunters need to select ponies whose parents have proven jumping abilities. Showing enthusiasts will look at the offspring of past champions, although there is no guarantee that a young horse will inherit his parents' qualities. Sought after characteristics can skip generations and full siblings are often very different.

Temperament is paramount. A stunning looking, beautifully moving colt with correct conformation but an unpredictable, aggressive or nervous nature is likely to lead to trouble. While it can be arguable to allow a colt to 'grow into himself', especially with Britain's slow growing native breeds, never be afraid to admit a mistake and geld a colt that isn't 'making the grade'. This is particularly important when it comes to temperament. The temperament of some colts can change with the flood of hormones that usually starts from the spring of their second year. If it all becomes just too much for them, they can become unpleasant to deal with or a danger to themselves as well as their handlers. At this point castration can be an answer. It's reassuring to know that every great gelding started as a top class colt.

Clifford Casino, a top class and consistently prize-winning Fell pony, was gelded as a ten-year-old.

What Age To Buy?

Exmoor herd on Dunkery

Older, established stallions do come up for sale every now and then. The pony's owners may have decided to retire from breeding or replace their stallion as he is 'coming into his own stock'. A mature pony can be a sensible choice for a first time stallion owner. The pony will have a performance record and it's likely that his offspring can be seen and assessed. Good animals often find new homes through word of mouth. It's worth asking breed society secretaries, committee members or established breeders for help and contacts. A wanted advert in the society website could also provide results. Respected breeders have a reputation to maintain so are unlikely to sell on anything unsuitable. Expect anyone selling or loaning a stallion to check out a new owner thoroughly. If they like and rate their stallion, they won't want him going to the 'wrong home'. It's always advisable to see a prospective competition pony performing in whichever discipline he is destined. Seek references, recommendations and advice.

A two-year-old colt can be a good prospect as he will be relatively well grown and can be better evaluated. Another benefit is that he still has a couple of seasons showing in youngstock show classes and can be used as a sire if licenced. A full vetting is recommended. Another option is for potential buyers to offer to pay for the cost of getting a colt licenced before going ahead with the purchase. Colts need to be vetted thoroughly before a breed society will licence them. Buying a two-year-old is an excellent choice in theory but finding a top class colt of this age can be like searching for hens' teeth. Good breeders with champion stock frequently have a waiting list of buyers. Their ponies are often sold as foals or the breeders hang on to the 'cream of the crop' to show and use themselves.

Buying a weaned foal or yearling colt is more of a gamble but more ponies are available so there's greater choice. It can be some consolation that they are usually cheaper.

4

Facilities

Entire ponies need to be kept in safe and secure surroundings. A colt or stallion on the loose can be a danger to himself, other ponies, handlers, property and the public. Even a weanling colt will rush off to introduce himself to other ponies. Uncut males are more likely to find any weakness in a fence or hedge than a mare or gelding. If they do get out and in with other horses, they may attempt to mount. Such behaviour will usually be met with a barrage of flying kicks. The potential for injury is very real. Accidents can happen so insurance throughout a stallion's life is a highly recommended precaution.

Ideally stallions should be turned out in paddocks with strong and sound, post and rail fencing. The height of the rails depends on the breed. Miniature Shetlands have different requirements to the largest native ponies. Check for broken rails daily and posts periodically for soundness.

Many stallions are turned out in a separate field to graze out of trouble. Most appreciate being able to see other ponies even if they can't get to them. Ponies are naturally herd animals that seek the company of their own kind. While some ponies are natural loners, most appreciate companionship.

The safest stallion paddock is one bordered by a post and rail fence that has a wide alleyway separating it from any neighbouring paddock fence. This parallel fence arrangement is most often seen in thoroughbred studs to prevent valuable horses from being able to touch any other horse and get injured but it is an uncommon precaution for native pony breeders.

Running a strand of electric tape or electric rope along the top rail of a post and rail fence is a good precaution especially with enthusiastic colts. It stops them leaning on a fence in an effort to get close to their neighbours. If a rail does inadvertently break or come loose, the electric tape is often enough to keep a stallion in place in the short term until repairs can be made. A second strand running between the top and bottom rails will stop a pony putting its head through the gap between the rails and rubbing out his mane. The grass is always greener on the other side and natives should have a full head and neck of hair!

If the plan is to use electric fencing on its own, accustom the pony to it first. A keen colt may run through an electric fence if he doesn't know to respect it. How many strands and how high to have them off the ground depends on the height of the pony. Ensure a stallion can't jump over or go under the wire and that the power is always on. Native ponies are canny and some learn when the power is off. If you do turn it off, when mucking out for instance, it is a good idea to leave it on occasionally. This keeps the ponies guessing. Mains power delivers a bigger kick and is better for stallions but not always viable. Maintaining electric fencing for entire ponies is the same as mares and geldings but just needs a bit more vigilance. If using battery power, it's best to have two batteries with one charged ready to swap when the other runs low. Solar powered units work well but a stand-by battery is a good idea in case there is a long spell of grey days. Anything that ensures there is never a stallion on the loose is worth the effort.

Sheep fencing, barbed and plain wire fencing are not designed for ponies and can result in permanent injury. Any form of metal wire fencing can bring a stallion's showing career to an abrupt end. Less critical but temporarily debilitating, manes and tails get pulled out on barbed wire and can take years to fully grow back.

A stallion's stable, like the fencing round his field, needs to be solidly built and in good repair. Kick locks should be fitted to stable doors in case the top bolt for any reason slides open. If a native pony mare or gelding breaks out, the likelihood is that they will head for grass. A stallion though will probably go visiting first. Anti-weave or full grills attached to a stallion's stable door can be used as an extra precaution. The use of grills depends on the age, experience and temperament of the individual pony. A half grill can be useful as a means of stopping a stallion leaning out and round to touch a neighbouring pony. Contact can unsettle one or both ponies. Precautions also need to be considered when leading a neighbouring pony out of its stable. A stallion may try to sniff, touch or even bite another pony within reach. Temporarily shutting the grill or top door of the stallion's stable will solve this problem. Stallions accustomed from a young age to being stabled next to mares, geldings and/or other stallions usually settle well. Some though can be territorial and need more personal space.

When booking stabling at shows, always inform the organisers that you are bringing a colt or stallion. Ask for a corner box and a gelding as a neighbour. Many people take lightweight, tie on grills with them to minimize the risks of a stallion jumping out, biting the public or other passing ponies. Grills can also stop the unwelcome feeding of titbits and warning signs help keep people at bay!

Living out 24/7 is the most natural choice for all British native ponies including stallions but is not always the most practical option. Time to relax, exercise and graze in a field is preferable. Colts and stallions benefit from the maximum turn out possible.

New Forest stallion, Brooks Hill Brumby

Early Years – The Yearling Colt

Native pony colt foals need to be registered with their breed society, micro-chipped and issued with a passport by the end of their natal year. Check with the relevant society for specific requirements and dates. It's a good idea not to leave registration to the last minute as secretaries get inundated. If they are going to be shown, all youngsters need full vaccination records in their passports.

Colts have been known to become sexually active at eight months old so most breeders separate them from mares and fillies before or around this age. If their dam is in foal again, colt foals can be left longer but should be weaned before the next foal is born or if the mare loses condition. Young colts need company and do well living with other male ponies. They need to grow, develop and learn their place within the hierarchy through play and social interaction. In the wild, colts live in bachelor groups until they are old enough to challenge a mature herd stallion.

In wild or feral herds, the older mares and herd stallion teach colts equine manners but in domestic situations the job can become the responsibility of their handlers.

Stallions see themselves as herd protectors out in the wilderness but domesticated ponies must learn that people hold a top position. Right from the beginning a colt must learn respect and look to his handler for leadership.

Many stallions and colts can forget their manners when around mares, especially those in season. A stud horse needs to learn that there is an appropriate time and place for covering. Many will be broken in for riding and when under saddle should be mannerly around people and other horses. Training for good behaviour should ideally start when a colt is a foal. It's important to be firm, consistent, understanding and kind. People need colts to trust them.

Feeding native pony colts differs little from geldings or fillies. If a colt becomes more difficult to handle when fed hard feed, it can be best to just give him a balancer and fibre forage. It's recommended to seek advice from a feed company's equine nutritionist. Native ponies thrive best on a fibrous diet. Keeping natives in peak condition, not too fat and not too lean, is an art. Each stallion is different and feeding regimes need to be worked out for the individual.

Training a colt is much the same as bringing on a mare or gelding. It's important that a colt doesn't learn bad habits or get away with unsociable behaviour while he is young. He should not be allowed to learn how to throw his weight around. Correcting behaviour that can lead to potential problems should begin from birth. Colts play by nipping, rearing, mounting and biting each other's forelegs among other antics. They must learn right from the start that people are not playmates. Mutual respected is paramount.

If a colt rears up near or at a person inviting play, a firm reprimand and handclap in his direction should put a stop to unwanted antics. Be aware that many will wheel away and throw up their heels in defiance. Be ready to step back out of striking distance. If a colt nips, a reprimand and handclap again should stop this behaviour. Pushing his head near his mouth sharply away is another method used. Biting, where the colt means to assert his authority, needs to be stopped as soon as possible. Male horses instinctively play and communicate through nipping and biting but they must learn right from the start that this behaviour is a totally inappropriate with people.

Stallions can get a bad press but with understanding they can be easier to deal with than fillies and mares. Take the time it takes and all the time they need. Give praise and reassurance when they have tried to please. They need to be a collaborators and friends who will do what's asked whatever the circumstances.

All youngsters, at some point, need to learn to wear a headcollar and accept restraint. As it's vital that colts learn manners from an early age, it can be beneficial to start them early. A well fitting, leather foal slip or halter is recommended, as it will break in an emergency. Remember to check the fit weekly and to adjust the halter straps as the colt grows. Patience wins every time.

There are no hard and fast rules for training a colt, just guidelines. Different people have different methods. Each pony is an individual. Some learn fast and some take more time. Some breeders run colts with stallion potential out on the hill or moor until they are three. It is can be easier to assess the colt's potential at that age but it's a good idea to get these youngsters well handled as foals. A totally untouched, three year old, large breed native pony colt that's been running 'feral' can be quite a challenge to work at first.

Teaching a yearling colt very basic training is a good idea. It enables the handler to develop a good relationship with the pony before he is too strong. Most colts enjoy the attention. Keep training simple at this age, keep it short and keep him interested with variation. Plan your training regime and allocate enough time. Ideally work with your colt every day for ten to twenty minutes for one or two weeks in a secure arena or paddock. How fast a colt learns will depend on previous handling, mental attitude, aptitude and maturity. Manners matter for a colt. It doesn't matter if he doesn't manage to do what is asked perfectly as long as he tries each new task. Don't frighten or over face him; remember he is only a baby. Introduce something new every day, like walking over a natural pole, past a plastic bag, through a puddle and so on. Don't ask too much in each session. Just one small step forward is enough. Always stop on a good note. Whips are for encouragement not for beating. Reward effort with lots of praise but not titbits as this can encourage a colt's natural tendency to nip.

Teaching a colt to concentrate on his handler and obediently complete simple tasks near other ponies is also good practice. It's much easier to establish respect when around mares at home rather than out at a show.

Once a yearling colt has learned over the course of a couple of weeks to calmly and quietly perform basic simple training tasks and be tied up in and out of a stable, he can be turned out to relax, play and grow. Unless he is coming in again for shows, this can be all he needs for his first year.

Yearling Highland colts, Murrayshall Geordie & Benedict of Dykes

As many native pony colts and stallions will be shown, it is useful to teach them 'ring craft'. They need to accept the tack they will wear in the ring. A yearling colt can be shown in a traditional, white, cotton, rope or webbing halter. The stronger, larger breeds may need a bridle with a mild bit. A colt should be under control at all times. He should walk quietly beside his handler and trot calmly but actively forward on command.

Native pony in white, cotton halter.

Make sure the pony is used to wearing rugs, travel boots and tail bandages before taking him to a show. Introduce him calmly at home to travelling in a horsebox or trailer, being washed and sprayed with show sheen (if used) and fly repellent. Yearlings often travel better with a companion but can then call for them when separated to enter the ring. Teach him sympathetically, small steps at a time and gradually build on the experience.

Choose a colt's first outing carefully. Go to a small show where there is plenty of space. Take a confident assistant with you who knows the pony. Arrive in good time. On arrival, park up and allow him to settle. Stand him securely and safely inside a trailer or horsebox with a haynet and don't leave him unattended. If he doesn't relax, starts kicking or threatens to rear, keep him calm, reassure him and return home; there's always another day. If possible take a nervous or over excitable colt to a professional yard where you can get help without the atmosphere of a show and build from there.

If your colt is calm on arrival at a show give him ten to twenty minutes to settle in the box or trailer. Many people then just lead their yearling colts around on the outskirts of a showground away from everyone else on their first outing. This way he can take in all the strange new sights and sounds in a calm and secure manner. A long lead rope can prove beneficial if a colt plays up. Those wishing to proceed into the show ring should collect in an area where there is plenty of space. Some collecting rings get over-crowded with other ponies. If this is the case, walk a colt calmly outside the collecting ring where there is sufficient room. Judges understand that colts need more space and will wait for an exhibitor to come from a little further away. When the relevant class is called, enter the show ring keeping a good distance from all other ponies. Colts and stallions 'talk' to other ponies to gauge their behaviour, status, sex and readiness to mate. This needs to be gently discouraged. Some yearlings show male behaviour early and can be enthusiastic about approaching other ponies. They must not be allowed to touch or even get close to other exhibitors. Close contact can cause a colt to rear in an attempt to mount. Other ponies may kick which can result in injury to handlers and animals. Your assistant can help by scouting and warning you if there is a mare in season or another colt playing up. Watch out for children charging happily about on their ponies and not always in total control. If there just isn't enough room, go home and try again at another venue.

In the ring keep plenty of space between your colt and the other entrants. Make good use of the corners to keep an adequate gap between you and the pony in front. You can circle round to the end of the line or move into a larger space. In the line up also give yourself plenty of room and if necessary stand your pony behind the line. Be prepared to excuse yourself to the judge and ask to leave the ring if your colt is upset, overexcited or misbehaving. You won't be thanked for upsetting other youngsters.

If a colt rears, step backwards keeping at his side and behind his shoulder. This is the best position to avoid being struck by a flailing front leg. It's also the best place to stand to prevent the possibility of the the pony getting a leg over the lead rein. If this does happens, when the pony comes back to ground, he will yank his mouth and may then shoot backwards. It's very hard to hold on to a colt in this situation. Try to take hold of the rein or rope near the bit so the loose end can be quickly retrieved from between his front legs. Not all stallions rear but it is a more common evasion in an entire pony than a filly or gelding. Stallions can be a little more unpredictable and they can be unexpectedly upset by unusual or unforeseen circumstances. Handlers should wear a hard hat and ensure the pony is wearing tack that he can be restrained in.

If a colt gets excited, he may well end up 'drawn' (with an erection). At a show, a small amount of Vicks rubbed round the outside of his nostrils can divert his attention, backing him up sharply or turning in tight circles can also be effective. Never use a cane on a colt's penis for displaying libido or interest in a mare. This can make the pony kick, distrust his handler and make him 'shy' to cover in hand if and when the time comes to use him as a stud horse.

Beware over showing a colt or stallion. To excel in the show ring, a pony needs to sparkle. A bored or tired animal will not look his best.

Judging a colt as a potential stallion takes an experienced eye. It's a matter of personal choice and there's an element of luck. Don't immediately write off a colt if he is placed down the line. Some need time to 'grow into themselves'. Many geldings go on to win championships galore with owners who wished they had kept them entire. On the other hand, there are also colts that win in yearling and youngstock classes but then do not grow on to reach expected or hoped for potential.

Dales pony

The Two-Year-Old Colt

Welsh pony in webbing halter with brass rings and chain

At two years of age, a colt can start to feel his strength and his hormone levels in the spring will probably be higher than when he was a yearling. Many people opt to remind a two-year-old of his basic lessons and manners. Depending on the pony this can take from a few days to a few weeks. Repeat all the simple lessons and tasks started as a yearling. The same principles apply – keep it varied, keep it short, stop on a good note and make a fuss when the pony is trying to do it right.

The equipment used depends on breed, size, development, temperament and the person dealing with the pony. Just as for a yearling, a two-year-old colt needs to be kept under control without restricting free and forward movement. The youngster should enjoy the training and learn to work with his handler.

The principles for training and breaking a colt are the same as for a filly, mare or gelding. Consult an expert for further guidance on training the young horse and refer to the numerous books available on the subject.

A two-year-old colt can be shown in a webbing or rope halter but all colts over two should be fitted with a bridle and bit. When showing in a bridle, a stallion roller/surcingle with single side rein can be worn. The side rein is attached on the offside from the bit ring to a D-ring on the roller. Show rollers are usually dark brown leather or coloured webbing with brass rings and leather buckle straps. The side rein discourages a colt from swinging round or nipping and provides more control. The colt can be led from the bridle with a leather lead rein attached to a brass Newmarket coupling chain with Walsall clips. Alternatively a straight brass chain with or without a black or brown rubber chain guard can be used. The guard helps with youngsters where a chain is too severe but a rope is not enough. Leather couplings are also available. The chain should be attached by the clip to the offside bit ring and pass through the near side bit ring. Many people wait until a colt is three or four years old, or even older, before fitting stallion tack. A stallion bit is often just fitted to older ponies. A roller can make some youngsters look immature while with others it can improve the overall appearance. Each pony needs to be evaluated as an individual.

Two year old Highland colt, Whitefield Lord Quincy, in stallion showing tack but with a mild bit as appropriate for a youngster

A two-year-old colt doesn't need to do too much work. Covering a couple of mares, being shown a few times and short periods of in hand schooling is usually sufficient. As with a yearling, a two-year-old will benefit from being turned out for most of the year, preferably with a companion, to grow on and develop naturally.

15

Further training is a progressive process through the life of any colt. Natives can continue to grow until they are five, six or seven but at three, colts are usually starting to feel their own strength and self-importance. Testosterone levels in the spring of their third year can be higher and they can be full of themselves. It is important to insist on respectful and mannered behaviour at this age. Stallions develop strong necks and powerful shoulders. They may 'try it on' by using their bulk and strength to get the upper hand. Lessons in moving away from pressure are a good idea for pushy colts. When leading a bargey colt, a cane directed into his shoulder can remind him not to invade his handler's space. Another effective tactic is to use a lead rope with chain attachment at one end. The chain goes through the bit rings and flicking it against the bit makes a noise that generally encourages the pony to move away from his handler. Practice at home. The show ring is not the place to start training.

A two-year-old colt can be used to cover his first mares but he must be licenced with his relevant breed society for his offspring to be registered. Each British native pony breed society has information and forms on their website. The colt must be micro-chipped, will be required to pass strict society requirements and undergo a thorough vetting.

All the relevant forms can be obtained from society secretaries. Contact details and information about the veterinary practice that will be used to do the vetting will need to be supplied to the society. Colts or stallions need to be clean, well handled and unshod for vetting. They will usually be required to wear a bridle, schooled to walk, trot and back up in hand. They may need to be exercised in such a way that will stimulate deep and rapid respiration (either ridden, lunged or free schooled). The vet will need to listen to their lungs and heart rate. A stable or darkened area is also usually required so that eyes can be examined and a level surface should be available for taking measurements.

A colt needs to have passed his licencing before he serves his first mares. Breeders should be aware that delays can occur when stallion licences are being processed and they should be applied for in good time before the stallion needs to be used.

If a stallion is refused a licence on veterinary or any other grounds, the owners will be entitled to a report from the relevant breed committee of the society. Some societies offer a grant for gelding a stallion that has been refused a licence. A veterinary certificate of castration is usually required by the society within three months of the notice of refusal. If the castration certificate and transfer to gelding papers are not received by the due date and no appeal has been lodged, the pony will usually be placed permanently on the relevant society X register (not registered as purebred).

Depending on the circumstance, a licence may be deferred. This is usually for up to a year and mostly for colts with one or more minor abnormalities that may resolve with age. After twelve months, if the owner considers the colt ready, a second inspection can be carried out. The society may require the examination to be carried out by the same veterinary surgeon or a veterinary surgeon from the same practice that was initially used. The owner is usually responsible for any additional veterinary fees.

An owner can elect to withdraw a colt/stallion from the licencing procedure before the veterinary inspection is complete. The society will then usually retain a minimal fee to cover administrative expenses.

If a licence is refused, the owner of the colt/stallion may be entitled to a further inspection by examiners elected by the society. This usually takes place not fewer than six months and not more than eighteen months after the first inspection. Sometimes an independent veterinary expert will be called in to give a second evaluation. The venue for any further inspection will be agreed between the society and the owner and all expense will be the responsibility of the owner. Appeals and additional fees usually have to be submitted within a date stipulated by the society, usually a month. If the appeal is successful, the appeal fee may be returned. If the appeal is unsuccessful, the same conditions apply as for the first refusal of licence i.e. proof of castration and any relevant fees for the transferal from stallion to gelding paperwork.

Licenced stallions can be put up for premium status. Premium schemes are designed to provide guidance and indicate good examples of breed conformation and type. Assessments are usually undertaken by a group of independent judges chosen by the society early each year. Owners must usually be full members of the society. All paperwork must be completed and fees paid. The stallion must be presented clean and well handled. He will need to be 'stood up' correctly, as well as walk and trot out in hand. Assessors may need to handle any part of the stallion and they may not all be present on a single day necessitating different assessor times and days. Spectators are not usually allowed and there will be no discussion between the owner and the assessors. Usually an average mark from all the assessors will be calculated. The society will set the pass mark. There is no right to appeal but a stallion can be represented for assessment (incurring an additional fee) usually after two years. Premium Stallion Status is recorded in the society studbook and website. It is an accolade and a good advert for a stallion.

There are various stallion performance awards. These are often evaluated and awarded at a relevant society recognised or organised event. They are tests to assess the performance and ability of a stallion. The standards, heights of the jumps and tasks vary to suit each breed. Full details can be found on the various native pony breed society websites.

Fell colt in appropriate halter

Breeding

There are many reasons for having a foal. Maintaining a rare breed or rare bloodlines may be the goal. Producing a quality purebred native pony is the aim of most breeders. If a good mare can no longer be exercised through no fault of her own, then breeding a potentially top-notch offspring from her is a viable project. Putting a mare in foal because she can't be ridden due to temperament or conformation faults is ill advised. If a children's pony mare has been outgrown, it's usually better to find a new home or break her for driving rather than putting her in foal. Mediocre mares generally produce average offspring and finding good homes for anything but the best isn't always easy. Don't breed if profit is your aim. Just breaking even can be a challenge.

Shetland ponies, Gue Jules and Gue Opal

Ponies can be infected by sexually transmitted diseases. Breeders should be aware of Contagious Equine Metritis (CEM), Klebsiella pneumoniae capsule types 1,2 and 5, Pseuodomonas aeruginosa, Equine Infectious Anaemia (EIA) and Equine Viral Arteritis (EVA). All of these diseases are transmitted venereally.

The frequency of testing and/or vaccination for these diseases is dependent on the level of risk and should be discussed with a vet. As a general rule, stallions considered to be 'high risk' are those that have not previously been used for breeding, have had a positive swab result in the past, have been on a premises infected with CEM/Klebsiella/Pseudomonas or have covered a mare that has not had a documented negative swab.

Owners are advised to test their stallions annually after 1st January every year and within twenty-eight days of the start of the breeding period. Any pony with a positive result will need to be treated under veterinary supervision and retested prior to breeding. Early testing is recommended to avoid potential delays and disappointments.

Stallions can be tested for CEM, Klebsiella and Pseuodomonas by taking two sets of swabs no less than seven days apart. Swabs need to be taken from three sites, the urethra, urethral fossa and penile sheath. Swabs must be taken by a veterinary surgeon. 'High risk' stallions may also need to be swabbed again after their first few matings. This should be discussed in conjunction with a veterinary surgeon.

EIA sometimes known as 'swamp fever' is a serious disease that is notifiable in Britain. It is transmitted through biting flies and contaminated blood products. Transmission via semen is uncommon but carries a potential risk. Symptoms range from serious illness to seemingly normal horses shedding the virus. There is no treatment or vaccination for the disease, and under current guidelines (December 2013) any horse testing positive for EIA will be subject to compulsory slaughter under the Infectious Diseases of Horses Order 1987. It is imperative that this disease does not spread within the UK horse population. Testing for EIA is done from a blood sample.

EVA is another disease transmitted venereally in horses and is also notifiable in the UK. Stallions are the main source of infection and once infected they can shed the virus in their semen. The best way to prevent infection is to vaccinate the stallion, however prior to vaccination ponies must be blood tested to check they are free from the disease. If a stallion has a negative blood sample he can then be vaccinated for EVA. If he has a positive result he must be isolated for at least twenty-eight days and not used for breeding activities until he has been examined by a veterinary surgeon under Defra (Department for Environment, Food and Rural Affairs) guidance to check he is not 'shedding' the virus.

Once vaccinated it is impossible to tell the difference between a vaccinated and infected pony. As a result all vaccination and blood sample results must be recorded in the pony's passport. Routine vaccination for EVA is recommended for stallions and teasers throughout Britain. Routine vaccination for mares is not generally advised. Deciding whether or not to vaccinate visiting mares depends on each stud's situation and past record. Vaccination and precautions for mares should be discussed with a veterinary surgeon.

Equine Herpes Virus (EHV 1, 4) is an endemic disease in the UK. This means that most ponies will come across it in their lifetime. There is no requirement to test for EHV in breeding animals in the UK but the disease is responsible for respiratory disease in youngsters and late term abortion in mares. In rare cases the disease can affect the nervous system and progress to paralysis. Management of breeding stock is the most important tool in controlling the spread of disease. Keeping pregnant mares separate and in small groups according to their due dates will help to minimise risk. Veterinary guidelines advise that stallions on breeding premises should be vaccinated with a primary course followed by six monthly boosters. It is recommended that pregnant mares are vaccinated at five, seven and nine months gestation.

As with all disease transmission, hygiene is an important method of preventing spread. Most viruses are neutralised by thorough disinfection. Good hygiene and paddock management should be maintained throughout a breeding premises.

Mares will only accept a stallion for covering when in season. All native pony breeders should be able to evaluate a mare's cycle - and it's not always a simple task. Generally mares stop cycling during the winter and start again in March/April when days get longer and the weather warmer. The ideal time for native pony foals to be born is April to June when spring grass helps the mare produce ample milk. The average gestation period is three hundred and forty days (eleven months and five days). Giving birth three weeks before or after the mare's due date is considered normal in ponies. The majority of mare owners will want to visit a stallion from April to July so the foal's birth coincides with the onset of spring grazing the following year. Mares are most fertile from April to July depending on the amount of daylight, as well as the quality and quantity of grass. A mare's cycle typically lasts twenty-one days with five to seven days (average is six and a half) in season and around fifteen days off. As a mare comes into season she will usually show some behavioural changes. She may call more to other ponies, be more affectionate or ticklish. Her temperature will change. She may show a sticky discharge from her vulva and it will probably be redder than normal internally. Mares are all different. Some display oestrus according to the textbook, others don't 'show' at all. The best way to access a mare's cycle, without getting her scanned by a vet, is to tease or test her with a stallion. Some will respond to a gelding particularly to one they don't know.

If 'in season' a mare will normally show interest in a male pony and react in various ways. She may prick her ears, call to him, squeal, adopt a typical breeding stance (flex her pelvis and stand with hind legs apart), urinate, lift her tail and show winking of labia and clitoris.

Mare adopting a typical breeding stance

The degree of response tends to increase as the mare approaches ovulation. Research has shown that fifty per cent of all mares exhibit heat five days before ovulation, seventy-five per cent at least three days before and ninety per cent at least forty eight hours before. The only way of predicting ovulation more accurately is by rectal palpation and ultrasonography (scanning) by a vet. The vet will measure the diameter of a developing follicle in an ovary. Most mares ovulate follicles ranging between forty and forty five mm forty-eight to twenty-four hours before the end of their standing heat (season). Follicular growth is approximately three to five mm per day, so a mare with a thirty-five mm follicle is likely to ovulate thirty-six to forty-eight hours after the scan. The vet doing the scan will be able to give the owner a good indication of ovulation. Although these parameters hold up for the average mare, follicle size at ovulation and the duration of oestrus in mares varies widely. Some mares might consistently ovulate thirty-five mm follicles, whereas others will not ovulate until the follicle has reached more than fifty millimetres in size.

Uterine edema (cartwheel pattern in the uterus seen on a scan) is an important indicator of oestrus and generally peaks around thirty-six hours prior to ovulation in healthy mares. The follicle wall may also thicken within twenty-four hours in eighty-five per cent of pre-ovulatory follicles. The rounded follicle may change shape forming a 'point' and appear more like a teardrop twenty-four hours prior to ovulation and should decrease slightly in diameter six hours before. Ultrasound may reveal visible 'leaking' of follicular fluid immediately before and during ovulation. If the mare has ovulated, she should be covered (mated) by a stallion within six hours. After twelve hours, positive pregnancy results decrease significantly even though the mare may continue to show signs of 'heat' for up to forty-eight hours after ovulation.

Some stud owners cover a mare on the third and fifth day of her season, others on the second, fourth and sixth if she is still 'in'. Records of a mare's previous cycles are helpful but only as a guideline. Some show season for just a couple of days and others up to ten or even twelve days. Temperature, climate, grass quality and age can all effect oestrus cycles. As most mares ovulate towards the end of their heat, covering on day one is generally regarded as a waste of the stallion's energy and an unnecessary risk. The stallion's sperm usually survives in the mare for forty-eight hours. If the stallion is not busy serving a lot of mares, the mare can be covered daily from day two until she goes 'off'.

A mare that has 'gone off heat' generally indicates that she has ovulated by putting her ears back, squealing, moving away from the stallion and swishing her tail irritably. Most stallions 'get the message' and desist from attempting to mount. They will continue to test their mares by vocalising (specific stallion calls) and nibbling but should not attempt to cover when her response is discouraging. A stallion that persists in pursuing mares no longer showing oestrus should be removed from the mare's presence to avoid aggressive behaviour and injury. There is little point trying to cover twelve hours after a mare has ovulated as successful fertilisation is then very unlikely.

Bay mare indicating to a stallion that she is no longer in season

Stallion owners should not accept mares for covering unless they arrive with up to date swab certificates showing negative results for various diseases. Alternatively confirmation of swab results can be confirmed by a vet or the testing laboratory. There are two common types of swab test. The majority of studs require mares to be swabbed for Contagious Equine Metritis (CEM) prior to natural covering. The swab can be taken at any stage of the mare's cycle, be sent from a veterinary surgery and assessed at a recognised laboratory. The swab results and certificate usually come back within ten days. CEM is a venereal infection of the genital tract of horses brought on by the Taylorella equigenitalis bacteria and passed on through sexual contact. It caused major problems of infertility in the equine breeding industry during the late 1970s but has now largely been controlled. The organisms that cause CEM are detected on a clitoral swab. All laboratories are required to inform Defra (Department for Environment, Food and Rural Affairs) of any cases they have detected.

The second swab that may be required is an endometrial (uterine) swab. This is taken to detect whether a mare has evidence of endometritis or infection of the lining of the womb. The swab has to be taken when the mare is in season and the results take about three days to come through. Endometritis is one of the most common reasons for mares having difficulty getting in foal. This swab is unnecessary in maiden mares but is advisable in mares that have had a history of being difficult to get in foal or have aborted a foetus. The two swabs can be taken at the same time if the mare is in season.

All visiting mares should be checked to make sure that they have not had a Caslick's operation. This procedure is not common in native ponies but owners of breeding stallions should be aware of the procedure. The operation involves trimming and sewing together up to eighty percent of the vulva. A Caslick's operation helps prevent faeces, air and bacteria entering a mare's reproductive tract. It's effective in reducing endometritis and increasing the chances of a pregnancy going to full term in mares with poor conformation of the vulva. A mare that has had a Caslick's operation needs to be cut open a month before a natural covering to allow healing.

Visiting mares should not have been in contact with any sick or infectious ponies prior to visiting the stud. They must have their hooves trimmed, hind shoes removed and be up to date with vaccinations and worming regime. Ideally and if feasible, mares should arrive a few days before they are due to come into season so they can settle into their new surroundings. Travelling an 'in season' mare can make them 'turn' and go straight out of season which means a three week delay before they can be covered.

Mares should be in good condition but not fat. Some people believe it helps to get a mare in foal if she is lean and gaining weight as she visits the stallion.

Highland stallion, Kyle of Croila

Covering In hand

Handling breeding stallions was traditionally seen as a job designated for men. Today more and more women are also getting involved especially with native ponies. The handler requires common sense, appropriate equipment and planning more than sheer strength. Most important the stallion needs training in restraint and respect for the handler. Sometimes a mare can be more of a handful!

Covering in hand is one of the most potentially dangerous endeavours associated with the care of ponies. The most important consideration for the ponies and handlers is safety. Do not try to cover a mare that is not obviously in season.

For in hand covering, a mare needs to wear a sturdy, leather bridle, a clean tail bandage and covering boots. Get her used to walking with the boots on before introducing her to the stallion just in case she tries to kick them off. While the use of hobbles and a twitch on the mare is commonly seen in Thoroughbred studs to protect valuable horses, it is not often a precaution needed for native ponies. Wash under the mare's tail and genital region gently with warm water to remove dirt and dung. Do not use soap, disinfectants, antiseptic lotions or any other applications. They can be invasive and cause severe skin and membrane irritation. Some also have a spermicidal effect.

At least two handlers are required for in hand covering and many studs use three. Handlers should wear hard hats with well fitting chin-straps, leather gloves and strong, stout boots with good grip on the soles. The stud pony should know and respect his handler. Hormones can turn a normally well-behaved colt into a hooligan. This is no time for lack of confidence or fear. Maintaining absolute control of the ponies is vital.

All ponies settle well into a routine and stallions are no different. It's a good idea to devise a covering regime that involves a selected site and procedure.

The stallion should wear a covering bridle. Many people use a bridle with a specific bit for covering. The stallion learns what to expect when wearing this bridle and is less likely to be confused if he is then broken for riding or driving. Some people use a Chifney bit as a safety precaution. While the bit has a severe action, an experienced handler will only use it if a colt or stallion needs controlling. A headcollar fitted with a chain under the chin can be enough for a quiet stallion. The handler needs a sufficient length of rope in order to stand at a safe distance during covering. All harness must be checked and be in good condition.

Lead the colt into the breeding area and walk him quietly around so he can see the mare but not get close to her. He will normally greet her vocally. The area must be large enough so that ponies and people have ample room. The ground or floor should have firm footing so neither animals nor people slip. Foals should be held by an extra handler quietly within sight and sound of its mother but well to one side to be kept out of harm's way. If the foal is stressed the mare will be too. So it's a balancing act of keeping both mare and offspring quiet but safe. No foal or handler should ever get between, in front of or behind the two adult ponies.

The mare handler should stand at her shoulder on the opposite side to the approaching stallion. The mare handler's duty is to steady the mare and prevent her from moving out from under the stallion or colt as he mounts.

If the mare starts moving do not place a hand on her shoulder, withers or back. As the stallion mounts, his front legs could injure the handler. Restrain her by the bridle or place a hand in front of her neck down her gullet line. If she takes a few steps the stallion will cope. If the mare won't stand still, lead her to and stand her facing a wall or secure fence so that she can't walk forward. Avoid corners and make sure the mare handler can step aside and get out of the way if need be. At no point should a handler or pony find themselves trapped. Do not cover a mare standing close and parallel to a fence as the stallion can hook a leg up on a rail as he dismounts.

The stallion handler should lead the stud pony calmly toward the mare at an angle where she can see his approach. He must be taught not to rush his job but be gentle with his mares. It's important that the handler is in control of the stallion at all times and not the other way around. Trying to charge around or past a handler indicates a lack of respect. The handler should always be aware of the stallion and immediately and firmly put a stop to him trying to charge a mare. This can be easier said than done with a very keen, big, young and strong colt. Control of a colt requires calm but firm understanding. Severe restraint can put off a keen colt but unruly behaviour can be dangerous. Rearing is one of the most often seen evasions. This is unsurprising as the pony is about to be asked to get on his hind legs to mount the mare. If the stallion rears away from the mare and charges forwards on his hind legs, pull him away. Circle away from the mare, calm everything down and when he is ready try again. Repeat the process until he learns that the only successful approach is a calm one. Some stallions are cautious in their approach. They nicker, nuzzle and sniff before mounting. Others like to get straight on with the job. It is a matter of balancing enthusiasm and restraint. Pawing is usually tolerated as a natural behaviour but striking out at a handler is unacceptable. The handler must be ready to step aside. A pony habitually trying to hurt his handler by striking, kicking or biting may have a temperament few would want to pass onto the next generation. Retraining or gelding are then options to seriously consider.

When covering with a two-year-old colt, make sure enough time has been allocated just in case things go awry. Colts can try to mount the wrong end so it's important they learn to approach from the rear but slightly from the side so the mare can see them. If a colt uses his strength and gets the better of his handler more than once, get help from more experienced stallion handlers before bad behaviour become a bad habit.

When all is calm, the stallion or colt can be allowed to sniff and nuzzle the mare's flanks and tail area but biting should not be tolerated. Habitual biters can be muzzled.

The flehmen response

A stallion may display the lip curling flehmen response as an involuntary reaction to her scent. He should drop his penis and maintain an erection ready for covering. A properly in season mare should urinate and adopt the covering stance but things don't always go to plan. Be prepared for one or either or the ponies to rear, bite, kick or attempt to run off. All the handlers must be well out of the reach of flying legs and be prepared to separate the ponies immediately.

If all goes well, the stallion will mount the mare for mating. A third handler can be ready to move the mare's tail to one side and if necessary guide the stallion's penis into the vagina. The third handler should step back and aside immediately their task is completed and get well out of the way. Mares can kick after covering and the colt or stallion will understandably want to get quickly out of her radius. To prevent injury, the mare handler should turn the mare to the left as the stallion dismounts and he should be backed away. Do not turn the mare to the right and stallion to the left (or vice versa) as you will end up with them rear to rear. This can result in a kicking match.

Mating/covering lasts an average twenty seconds in ponies. During ejaculation the stallion may flag his tail up and down. As the stallion mounts his penis elongates a little and narrows to the end probably to facilitate an easier entry to the mare. As he ejaculates the penis head (flange) swells, though it is more spongy than hard, to serve as a temporary plug of the cervix encouraging semen to remain in the uterus as long as possible. Stallions ejaculate into the uterus itself. Of the five to seven jets of semen during ejaculation, at least the first three or four should enter the uterus. Seminal fluid at the final stages of equine ejaculate tends to be thick and glutinous. This also helps to prevent leakage. The enlarged head of the stallion's penis is a good indication of successful ejaculation but the only sure way to test is to collect a semen sample. A drop is sufficient for immediate examination under a microscope. Native pony breeders usually only ask a vet to do the procedure when testing a stallion's fertility.

It's recommended that a stallion's penis should be thoroughly rinsed with clean warm water after a covering/service to help prevent venereal infection. Colts need to be introduced to gentle washing at a young age so that this becomes part of their normal routine. It is also important to regularly examine the penis and sheath for any signs of Equine Coital Exanthema (ECE). This is a type of herpes virus and causes lesions on the genitals similar to 'pox-like' craters. If these are found, the stallion should be rested from sexual activity until the lesions resolve, usually after ten to fourteen days. Treatment (if any) is palliative rather than curative. It can consist of daily cleansing of the genitalia to reduce inflammation and prevent secondary bacterial infection.

Covering maiden mares needs more time as they can be anxious and frightened. Never try to cover for the first time in a rush. If the mare is too nervous to stand, seek veterinary advice to determine the stage of her cycle. If she is properly in season with a well-developed follicle and still won't stand, the vet may recommend sedation.

If the stallion lacks libido, lead him away to watch the mare for a while from a distance or let him see but not touch other mares. This can help get cautious stallions 'in the mood'. Be patient, some stallions get frustrated with their own inability and that can make them misbehave. If this tactic fails to get him interested take him away, give him a good rest, a drink, some hay and try again later. If he remains totally unenthusiastic seek veterinary advice. Hock or back pain can make a pony reluctant to take weight on his back legs. A stallion that has been kicked and hurt by a mare may be reluctant to go near them. Sometimes giving them a year off from breeding can resolve the problem.

Dartmoor stallion,
Moortown Statesman

Paddock Breeding

The most basic method of breeding ponies is to turn a colt or stallion out with his mares. In the New Forest this is general practise each summer. This may seem uncomplicated and as nature intended but it does have risks. Out in the wild or open spaces like the New Forest, the ponies have ample space and the stallion will have several mares to occupy his attention. If a mare isn't in season, he will move on to the next leaving alone those that reject his interest. In a confined field with just one mare the situation is rather different. An excited stallion rushing towards a potential mate can appear intimidating especially to a maiden mare. A frightened mare will lash out and can easily injure an over-enthusiastic, inexperienced colt. Panicked mares can jump out of fields or crash through fences to get away from a zealous stallion. Turning out a stallion and mare into a field bordered by barbed wire is a serious accident waiting to happen. In a herd situation, some mares guard the stallion keeping others away. This can lead to all sorts of shenanigans with the stallion trying to get to a receptive mare and the jealous mare putting herself between them or driving off her rival. In this situation the possessive mare needs to be separated into a different field until all the other mares are in foal. 'Pasture breeding' is easiest with an older, experienced stallion that knows to keep a polite distance from mares that are not in season.

Fiona of Silverstripe and Murrayshall Geordie

All ponies need to have neat, trimmed hooves to minimise the risk of injury if they kick. The mares need to have negative swab tests. It's advisable that the ponies wear leather head collars so they can be caught if need be. Headcollars can be removed after covering when all ponies involved have settled. The mare's tail can be bandaged but tail bandages must not be tight or be left on for more than a few hours. Restricting blood supply to a pony's tail can result in loss of pigmentation (grey hairs), severe loss of hair and permanent damage to the tail. Keep a close eye on the mare to check the bandage hasn't come loose and is trailing on the ground. It may be worth considering cutting a little off the mare's tail if it is very long. Native pony mares often lose some of their long, thick tails during covering. As they lower their quarters adopting a mating stance, their tail trails on the ground. When the stallion dismounts after mounting, he can tread on the mare's tail and pull some of it out. Alternatively the skirt of the tail (the long hair) can be folded and secured with a bandage or tape but must not be left like this more than an hour.

If the plan is to run a two year old colt out with a mare, it's preferable to start with an 'in season' experienced brood mare without a foal at foot. In the excitement of encountering his first mare, a colt may try his best to cover her whether she is ready or not. Frustration can lead to excessive chasing, tying up and a mare trying to escape through fences. Both ponies may end up hurt, exhausted and stressed. A stressed mare is less likely 'to hold' in foal even if she is successfully covered. Introducing a young stallion to a mare in her second day of season is usually less problematic. On the first day, some mares may only just have come into season and may not be relaxed enough to stand quietly for covering.

When the mare shows signs of being properly in season and interested in the stallion, prepare to introduce the two ponies. A handler should take the colt to the far end of the field away from the gate wearing a bridle over his leather head collar. Distract him with some food while a second handler brings the mare into the field through the gate. Both handlers need to be co-ordinated and know exactly what is expected of each other before introducing the stallion to the mare. Handlers do not want to be caught in the middle of the two loose ponies when they first meet. Neither do they want to leave one pony trailing a lead rope. Pre-planning and communication for all the people involved is key to a successful pasture covering. The mare handler can release the mare as soon as possible after entering the field having indicated the intention to do so to the stallion handler. The bridle should be slipped off the stallion at the same time as the mare is released. On releasing the ponies, the handlers should immediately leave the field or stand well out of the way. The ponies may well show off, buck, kick out, rear and gallop about. They will not be concentrating on the people in attendance.

Except in an emergency, no attempt should be made to interfere with the ponies. After an initial flurry of excitement, the mare will usually stand to be covered. If she continues to kick or run, it's likely she is not in season or not yet ready to be covered. If this is the case, catch the ponies as soon as is it safe to do so. This is usually when they tire and need a breather. Distract the stallion with food if necessary. Slip a bridle on and while he is eating remove the mare from the field. Tease her again either later that day or the next morning. If she then appears in season, try her again with the stallion but if she still won't stand to be covered have her checked by a vet. Some mares will stand to allow the stallion to mount but then immediately walk off or round in tight circles. This prevents the stallion from covering and can make him frustrated and even aggressive. One way to overcome this situation is to stand by the gate outside the field with a bucket of pony food. Make sure you allow the stallion enough time after a previous attempt to cover the mare before trying this tactic. How much time is needed between attempts to cover will depend on the stallion. Some will be keen to mount again after five minutes if they haven't ejaculated. Other stallions may require up to an hour. Bandage the mare's tail first if safe to do so, then attract the mare over to the gate by shaking the bucket of food. Encourage her to eat from the bucket with her head over the gate. As she puts her head into the bucket calmly take hold of her headcollar. Do not clip a lead rope onto her headcollar. If she really does not want to be covered and takes off, she will end up trailing a rope.

Take hold of the side of the headcollar with one hand and allow the mare to take a mouthful of food. Then put down the bucket and hold both sides of her headcollar while reassuring and steadying her. In this situation the mare cannot walk forward and can usually be prevented from turning around. Holding her firmly up against the gate, encourage the stallion by calling him over. There's a good chance he will mount and cover her successfully. Use food as a lure to the mare when the stallion is grazing some way away. If the stallion comes charging over for the food, let go of the mare immediately and take the bucket well away. Use a helper to distract or hold the stallion if appropriate. If the mare will still not stand or kicks when held but is in season have her checked by a vet.

After covering, some breeders immediately lead the mare out of the covering paddock or yard and walk her for twenty minutes. This prevents her from squatting, straining and leaking seminal fluid. In the wild or when running with a stallion, mares will lose what appears to be quite a lot of fluid after each mating. This is normal and not usually a cause for concern, it only takes one sperm to fertilise an egg.

If facilities are available, some breeders put a stallion in one field and mares in an adjacent field separated by a strong, wooden post and rail fence. Mares and stallions can strike and kick when first introduced so every precaution should be made to minimise the risk of legs getting caught or hooked over fences and gates.

A stallion kept in an adjacent paddock to mares can be expected to pace the boundary at first and call frequently. He will usually settle down and get used to the regime but can lose weight - a consideration for those who want to show their stallion later in the season. While the mares will be closely watched by the stallion, they will usually only pay him attention when they come into oestrus. Mares wandering over to the stallion, staying near him and showing signs of season can be allowed into the stallion's field. A handler should lead the stallion away from the gate while the mare is brought in to the field as outlined above.

Mares are often teased by leading them to a gate with the stallion on the other side. To avoid the risk of getting a leg caught, bring the mare close to but not right up to the gate. Then if she strikes with a front leg she is less likely to put it through the bars. The handler should stand to one side at the mare's shoulder so that he or she is not at risk of being struck by a flailing limb. Never force a mare to get closer to a stallion than she wants to be. A standoffish mare is indicating that she is not in season. Teasing mares over a stable door is also used. The door should be securely shut and in good repair. Most studs that tease in this way have a taller than usual stable door to discourage any attempt by the stallion of jumping out.

Once a mare has been covered she can be left in with the stallion but the pair need to be watched. The tail bandage, if used, should be removed. Some stallions over cover their mares sometimes up to every thirty minutes. In this situation the quality of the stallion's sperm will diminish and he may well lose weight. The mare can get sore, particularly across her back from bearing the unaccustomed weight of the stallion. She may end up with a 'dirty' uterus from retained excess seminal fluid. The end result can be reduced fertility. To avoid these problems some breeders, even when covering loose in a paddock, bring the mare to the stallion and only cover her once a day or every other day until she is 'going off'. In between covering, the ponies are separated. The mare can be left permanently with the stallion when she shows signs of going out of season. These signs are usually squealing, striking out with a front leg, putting her ears back or humping at the stallion. She may still stand for covering but isn't so relaxed about the situation. A two-year-old colt may still chance his luck when a mare has gone out of season but the mare will make it plain that his advances are now unwelcome. There is a risk of the colt being bitten and kicked but the ponies usually settle after a while. One advantage of running a colt with a mare is that conception levels can be higher. Another is that the colt learns respect, manners and how to behave around mares. He is also not condemned to a solitary life which can lead to negative behaviour traits. All stallions enjoy companionship and need plenty of exercise to keep them both happy and fit.

Highland stallion, Murrayshall Geordie with Lochlands Mandola

Testing A Mare For Pregnancy

It is common for a mare to remain at the stud until pregnancy is confirmed. Pregnancy can be ascertained by testing for signs of season in the mare. She can be presented to a stallion fourteen days after her last covering and daily for the next week. If the mare clearly demonstrates season she is unlikely to be in foal and most owners will want her covered again. Some mares squeal and urinate as a reaction to the stallion but fidget and do not adopt the typical breeding stance. This behaviour can indicate that the mare is coming into season or is responding to the continued release of progesterone, the hormone essential for the maintenance of pregnancy. Even though she has conceived, the mare will continue to ovulate in a normal twenty-one day cycle until the embryo implants into the uterine wall. The mare's reaction can be confusing and lead to false alarms. A pregnant mare though should not accept a stallion for covering and generally rejects any advances. Care should be taken when teasing pregnant mares as some can react very aggressively to the stallion. If she remains standoffish between fifteen and twenty days after her last covering, she can be assumed to have 'held at three weeks'. Some owners wait for a further cycle and then tease her again with the stallion. If she again shows no sign of season, she is said to have held at six weeks and presumed in foal. At this point the stud horse owner has completed his or her commitment. A covering fee is then usually owed depending on individual arrangements.

If the mare comes back into season and pregnancy remains the aim, cover her again. If she comes back into season a third time she will need to be examined by a vet. The most common cause of infertility is overweight, underweight, stress or infection. Natural covering is a relatively 'messy' process and can result in a 'dirty mare'. A 'dirty mare' is one that has a uterine infection and/or retained fluid. The normal response of the equine uterus to insemination is an inflammatory reaction producing uterine fluid. Reproductively healthy mares normally clear the inflammation through the cervix within twenty-four to forty-eight hours. If the uterus fails to 'flush' naturally the mare can develop endometritis (infection/contamination). Post-mating endometritis can make the uterus an inhospitable environment and reduce the likelihood of embryo implantation. The incidence of post-mating endometritis is higher in older, maiden mares.

Prevention of infection can be achieved by flushing the mare's uterus with warm sterile fluid with or without antibiotics post covering. This is done by a veterinary surgeon who will pass a sterile tube into the uterus and infuse sterile fluid through it. The fluid is then siphoned out immediately and repeated until it comes back clean. At this point antibiotics can also be infused if the veterinary surgeon thinks this is necessary.

The initial flush is normally done four to twelve hours post insemination and can be repeated every twelve hours if necessary for up to seventy-two hours (depending on when the mare ovulated). Oxytocin is often injected at the same time as flushing to induce uterine contractions and encourage expulsion of this uterine fluid.

'Flushing' by a vet is possible because once semen has been deposited within the uterus, enough strong swimming sperm will reach the oviduct (fallopian tube) within four hours. It only takes one sperm to fertilise a recently ovulated and waiting egg/follicle. A fertilised egg is not re-released into the uterus until approximately half way through the fifth day after the mare came into season. Flushing the uterus while the egg is in the fallopian tube will not result in 'washing' an embryo away.

If the mare checks out as healthy, cycling normally and with no obvious physical abnormalities or problems, the stallion will need to be examined. The easiest way to test a stallion's fertility is for a vet to collect a small sample of seminal fluid after covering. This will be checked under a microscope for sperm count and mobility.

Teasing gives a good indication of pregnancy but for definite confirmation the mare needs to be scanned by a vet. Stallion owners should keep careful records of the mare's cycles and covering dates. The owners of the mare can then assess when to get her scanned. This is usually from fourteen or fifteen days after the last covering. If the mare is scanned not in foal and not 'dirty', she can go back to the stallion to be covered again. The vet can also measure follicle size and estimate the approximate time of the next ovulation. A scan at fourteen to eighteen days is also a good time to detect twins. Twinning in horses occurs in about ten percent of all equine pregnancies and seventy per cent of those are naturally reduced by day forty of the pregnancy. Twins pregnancies are undesirable as the outcome is usually late term abortion of both foetuses. Apart from the death of one or both twins, the consequences of late term abortion can seriously affect the mare and may cause retained placenta, dystocia, delayed uterine involution and metritis. The earlier twin embryos are detected the easier it is to abort (pinch) one out without damaging the other. After eighteen days the procedure is much more technically demanding and the risk of losing both embryos is higher.

A pregnancy can be aborted or reabsorbed, often with no obvious clinical signs, between the first scan and thirty-five days after the last day of a mare's season. Many breeders rescan a mare between thirty-five and forty-two days. The embryo implants at approximately day thirty-five and after this time a pregnancy is less likely to be lost. A heartbeat can also be visualised at this stage and is a good but not infallible sign of a healthy foetus.

Mare owners will need a covering certificate from the stallion owner to successfully register their foals with the appropriate native pony society. The covering certificate should record the last date of covering. If foaling dates differ more than five weeks away from the expected dates, registration of the foal may be queried by the society.

Welsh pony, Lilford Cariad Fack

Artificial Insemination (AI)

Anyone thinking of going down the Artificial Insemination (AI) route needs to work closely with a veterinary practice experienced in collecting semen from breeding stallions.

Any semen to be used for AI originating from within the UK should be accompanied by a certificate stating that it is free from Contagious Equine Metritis (CEM), Klebsiella pneumoniae capsule types 1,2 and 5, Pseuodomonas aeruginosa and Equine Infectious Anaemia (EIA) and that the stallion has either tested negative for, or is vaccinated against Equine Viral Arteritis (EVA). All of these diseases are transmitted venereally, therefore it is essential that semen used for breeding purposes is free from them. Certificates can be downloaded from the Horserace Betting Levy Board website, www.codes.hblb.org.uk.

A stallion used for AI needs to be calm and cooperative. He should accept washing and handling of his penis so that the introduction of an artificial vagina (AV) won't upset him. It's easier to train for AI in the normal breeding season (end of April to beginning of August).

There are two established methods for collecting semen. One uses an in season mare and the other a dummy. The former usually requires synchronisation of a mare to induce ovulation so she will stand to be covered. This is achieved by injecting the mare with Prostaglandin hormone such as Cloprostenol (Estrumate, MSD Animal Health), the use of Gonadotrophin Releasing Hormone (GnRH) analogues such as Deslorelin implants (Ovuplant, Dechra Veterinary Products)) or human Chorionic Gonadotrophin (hCG) hormone (Chorulon, MSD Animal Health).

The second involves a dummy mare. When training a novice stallion to mount a phantom mare (a dummy) several factors need consideration; e.g. the number of people on the training team, the choice of artificial vagina and restraining equipment, the availability of stimulus mares, and the dummy mount. It's recommended that a pony stallion should be at least three years old for AI training. Training for semen collection requires patience. It can take between a few days to several weeks. Keep it simple and as stress free as possible. Don't expect to sell any semen samples until the stallion is relaxed about the procedure and cooperatively trained. Samples collected during training or during hot weather can result in a poor quality result. Safety precautions described for covering in hand apply with AI collection. With patience, a well-behaved and workmanlike breeding stallion, providing quality semen samples, is an achievable end result.

The breeding arena needs to be a spacious area dedicated to AI. Stallions soon learn what is required of them if there are no distractions. The people and place need to be consistent to avoid confusion. A dummy mare must be strong enough to support the stallion's weight and be well padded so that stallion is never uncomfortable or hurt. Phantoms or dummies often have a rigid body supported on a single strong post. They need to be a suitable height and size for the breed of pony. A stallion needs to be able to balance on the dummy and have a big enough structure to grip. The covering material must not tear easily. The flooring should be level and must not be loose or slippery. The AV should fit the individual stallion. Care must be taken with temperature, lubrication and pressure. Expert veterinary advice is essential.

Urine from an oestrus mare is often used to stimulate the stallion to mount the dummy. Each stallion is different. Those that are eager to mate are usually easier to train. Some prefer a mare present, others perform without and some won't mount a dummy at all. If a mare is present, she should be out of the way, behind a teasing wall or in a stable. Two handlers are needed. The first holds the stallion and the second the AV. Both need to be confident pony people who treat the stallion with respect as well as authoritative encouragement and patience.

The stallion should wear his specific breeding halter or bridle. He must be allowed to be enthusiastic but in a mannerly way. As he drops his penis he can be washed. The AV should be filled with water at 47° Celsius and be semi tight. Temperature and pressure can be altered to suit the specific stallion. As the stallion mounts when led to the dummy his erection is diverted into the AV. After ejaculation the AV is taken to the laboratory. Both handlers should stand on one side of the dummy so they can co-ordinate their actions. Both must wear protective headgear. Protective but not restrictive clothing and footware is advised.

Whether you use live cover or AI, a stallion's career at stud depends on his fertility, usually assessed by the number of mares he successfully gets in foal. Fertility is increased if the stallion is in good health, disease free and unstressed. All stages of breeding need to be a positive experience for an entire pony.

Running Male Horses Together

Ponies are naturally herd animals and seek company whatever their sex. In the wild, a single dominant stallion will run with a group of mares chasing away rival males for as long as he is able. Subordinate, young or old stallions and colts form all male bands. Native pony stallions can live or over winter together as long as there are no mares in the near vicinity. Colts should be introduced to future companions or a male herd as weanlings or yearlings. They soon form a hierarchy and learn to know their place and keep out of trouble. The same applies to a stallion running with a gelding. After the covering season, some studs turn a stallion out with a gelding for company. Again, it is advisable to introduce the two ponies together as youngsters.

Individuals that don't know each other should be introduced slowly. Keep them separate but close to each other until they are well acquainted before turning them out together. There is risk involved just as there is introducing a new mare or gelding to an established group or individual. If there is determined fighting, separate the ponies at the soonest safe opportunity. Just like mares and geldings, stallions choose their friends.

Shetland stallions, Brandon Fiery Jack, Gue Handsome and Gue Kyle

Stallions'
dung heap

Stallions use communal dung piles. In the wild this behaviour signals the presence of each individual stallion and forms a means of communication between harem stallions and bachelor groups. In this way they all know of each others' whereabouts and can avoid conflict. Dominant stallions urinate over the dung of their mares to signify ownership. It's also thought that the high level of pungent cresols in stallion urine helps mask the scent of oestrus mares and so illicts less attention from rival males.

Stallion marking mare's dung

Castration

Sometimes it is not in a colt or stallion's best interest to keep him entire. He may no longer be needed for breeding, could have sustained an injured or not have the right temperament. Gelding can be done at any stage but the medical risks increase with age. A closed castration conducted under controlled sterile hospital conditions is generally recommended by vets as the most suitable operation for stallions (over four years of age). A closed castration does add the associated risks of general anaesthesia and is more expensive than a standing castration (depending on the size of the horse).

Gelding a stallion to eliminate bad behaviour doesn't always work but is often worth a try. Re-schooling, groundwork and going back to basics may sort out behaviour problems as well. Castrated stallions need to be separated from other ponies for at least a month. After this time they should be carefully monitored until they settle down. Stallion attitude and behaviour can continue for between three months and a year as the male hormone, testosterone, clears from the pony's system. Most late gelded ponies go on to behave like any other gelding. Some continue to be interested in mares and may even try to cover them, and a few continue to be aggressive to other geldings. Most though go on to lead normal, happy and useful lives.

Exmoor gelding,
Tawbitts Euan

Working Pregnant Mares

A pregnant mare can be ridden but there is a risk of miscarriage or reabsorption. Strenuous exercise is best avoided and a mare should not be ridden for the last three months of pregnancy. If she is turned out with a stallion, be aware that the colt or stallion will not want 'his' mare taken away. Some stallions think that putting a headcollar on a mare is a signal that you want her covered. The easiest solution is to have a helper who can put a bridle on the stallion and hold him while the mare is led from the field. Distracting the stallion with a little food can help proceedings. Another option is to divide the field with electric fencing. The stallion can be led into the section of the field away from the gate. Providing him with some food as a distraction when the mare leaves can keep proceedings calm. Leave the stallion where he is while the mare is away. Return her after exercise and allow the pair to greet over the electric fence. The stallion will quickly recognise that this is 'his' mare and not a new one coming for covering. When all is calm, the two ponies can run together again. If the ponies are being fed hay, putting two heaps well apart out in the stallion's section just before allowing the mare to join him can also distract them. The stallion will soon learn to accept the mare coming and going.

Highland mare, Fiona of Silverstripe and stallion, Murrayshall Geordie

Working Stallions

A performance career is important for many stallions in order to 'prove' and advertise their temperament and abilities. Many people only use a stallion for breeding when his showing career is over. Other people combine both careers and many stallions cope well. Many happily learn to work around mares in the covering area as well as remain mannerly in the show ring or stable yard. It helps to cover in one specific area so the stallion knows which job is required in which place. Some stallions don't cope at all with combining covering and riding duties so they show one year and breed the next. Others only stand at stud early in the breeding season, covering a limited number of mares. The stallion then goes to another yard after his covering duties are over to concentrate on ridden work. As with all things equine, it depends on the temperament of the individual pony.

While general training and handling should be the same for stallions, geldings and mares, it's beneficial to establish a good one-on-one relationship with a native pony colt or stallion. Most are sensitive, keen to please and enjoy human company. If you can win their trust, the reward can be a special, long-term partnership.

Fell stallion,
Lunesdale Mountain Mist

Connemara colt,
Galloon Rollover

In Conversation With…

Carole Laignel
Shetland Ponies

Carole with Gue Stud foals

Carole Laignel has Shetland ponies in her blood. Her family has bred them for generations. The ponies take up almost all of Carole's spare time and are one of her greatest passions. She is secretary of the Pony Breeders of Shetland Association and a council member of the Shetland Pony Stud Book Society.

Carole runs the Gue Stud that was established on the Shetland island of Unst in the 1800s and which is now based in Dunrossness, South Shetland. Her great grandfather had entries in the first Shetland pony studbook of 1891 and many of her current stock can trace their pedigrees back to entries in those first records.

Small ponies have been on the Shetland Islands for at least two thousand years. Archaeological finds date back to the Bronze Age and it is believed that the Shetland pony has been in domestic use since this time. The smallest ponies were those that thrived best in Shetland's harsh winters, wild maritime weather and with meagre fodder. The conditions on the islands ensured the survival of the fittest and goes towards explaining why the Shetland pony is so hardy. Nowhere on Shetland is further than four miles from the sea and it is legendary that hungry ponies would eke a living eating seaweed washed up on the seashore. Some still supplement their feed in this way. Isolation has meant little outside influence from other breeds.

Carole's father with Goldie of Gue at the 1971 show in Unst

"My great grandfather was one of a fairly small group of Shetland pony owners who registered their stock. Initially the Gue ponies would have been put to use on the croft for example for carrying baskets of peat down from the hills, pulling ploughs and also for carrying people. Back in the 1800s standard Shetlands were bred at Gue and these ponies, particularly the males over four years old came to be in great demand for working down the coal mines. Many ponies from Shetland were exported to work in collieries when children were banned from working underground. The Shetland pony was probably chosen both because of its size and also because of its legendary strength. A Shetland pony can pull twice its weight. Ponies also began to be exported, some as far afield as America and Australia.

"In the past, ponies, like sheep and cattle, were part of the farm stock. As a small child I helped my father and uncle herding ponies off the hill for the annual sales. The youngsters, although handled a little, wouldn't have had a halter on until shortly before the sale. Things are different now but I am trying to carry on the family tradition of breeding good Shetland ponies. My aim is to produce ponies that go back to Gue bloodlines. While achieving this, I have realised that I go for a particular type as all my ponies go back to Marshwood and, all but one, Berry bloodlines.

"I breed miniatures because I like their overall conformation and find them a pleasure to handle. I started off breeding mainly chestnuts but have diversified into different colours and now have quite a few blacks, bays and skewbalds.

"I have about thirty ponies including five stallions. Three of the 'boys' are imported to outcross my bloodlines. Kirkstall Achilles and Brandon Fiery Jack both came up from the Tawna Stud in Cornwall. They came by truck to Aberdeen and then had a twelve-hour ferry journey to Shetland. They both travelled well but I was slightly worried about Jack. When he arrived in April, he had lost his winter coat. All the ponies up here were still holding on to theirs but thankfully he didn't have a problem. Shetlands are tough.

Kirkshall Achilles

"**Kirkshall Achilles** (Mardlebrook Dancer x Kirkstall Ursula, 32.5") is a lovely bay skewbald who fits well with my mares for colour, size and bloodlines. Piebald is fashionable at the moment but I prefer skewbald, especially bay ones. I am delighted with my first foals by Achilles. I showed two of his foals locally this year and they won a first and second at the first show followed by the same at the other show only placed the opposite way around.

"**Brandon Fiery Jack** (Birling Benjamin x Brandon Filigree) is chestnut and my smallest stallion standing at 30.5". He was fifteen when he came up here and has sired some super foals. Jack is renowned for his long mane that almost reaches the ground.

50

"**Lignite Chickadee** (Kerswell Basil Brush x Rowans Berry Cascade, 31"). Chico is a five year old, smart, red bay that has done well when shown on the mainland. I am really looking forward to his foals next year.

"My homebred stallions are all show winners or from champion parents.

"**Gue Kell** (Zorro of Berry x Gue Delight) is a bright chestnut, blond-maned, 32", four-year-old who passed his V V E (voluntary vetting evaluation) this year. He has a lovely nature and great conformation but he has a very greedy streak. He is always poking his head through fences to get at the grass on the other side and loses part of his mane in the process. I would like to put him through the evaluation process so I will have to try and find a solution to this.

"**Gue Icon** (Ewan of Houlland x Gue Delight, 32") won a silver award last year as a junior stallion. He is a chestnut, traditional stamp of a pony with loads of bone and super conformation.

"**Gue Kyle**, a well-marked skewbald has been sold to my partner. Standing at 36.75", he's a bit big for my stud so may be sold on or we may geld him and just enjoy showing him. Kyle has a wonderful temperament.

"In the springtime I select which stallions will run with which mares. This depends

Gue stallion herd

on bloodlines or, for example, putting a finer boned mare with a strong boned stallion. I am lucky to have enough land to run them out in separate groups. Once the mares have all foaled, the stallions get turned out with 'their' mares for six to eight weeks. I need all the foals born by early June to allow them to be weaned before the annual pony sale in Lerwick in October. My best colts are sold as potential stud stallions. The rest are usually gelded and used as small riding ponies, companions for larger horses or kept as pets.

"Apart from the few covering weeks the stallions mostly run together. There tends to be an established hierarchy so they all know their place. I breed ponies with good temperaments so they all have great natures and their own characters. I definitely have more stallions than I actually need but am very fond of 'my boys'. They are very affectionate, such fun ponies and their antics make me laugh. What could be better than that?"

Gue youngsters

Willie and Jean Ralston
Highland Ponies

**Jean working with colt
Moss-side Uilleam Mor**

Willie and Jean run a small Highland pony stud based at Moss-side Farm, Methven, Perth, Scotland. They have owned Highland ponies for over thirty years and bred them under the Moss-side prefix for nearly twenty-five. They successfully produce good quality, strong, traditional Highland ponies and have enjoyed an excellent show record both in hand and under saddle. They have some youngstock for sale and visitors are welcome by appointment. At present their senior stallions are:

Moss-side Domhnach (258/94 Strathmore Concorde x Iona O'Kinnoull,13.3.1/2 hh). Domhnach is a very traditional pony with great bone, straight action with a very good length of stride. He had great success in the show ring both in hand and under saddle. His temperament is excellent as is his fertility. He is from prizewinning parents Strathmore Concorde and Iona O'Kinnoull. His foals are strong boned with super pony heads. Domhnach has sired the most registered foals of any Highland pony stallion over the last thirteen years.

Moss-side Domhnach

Moss-side Iain Mor (79/99 Rhuaridh of Mendick x Moss-side Breagh,14.2 hh). Iain Mor is exceptional for his lovely straight action and elevated paces. He has a good head, wonderful temperament and excellent bone. He is by Ruaridh of Mendick and Moss-side Breagh - both in hand and under saddle winners. Iain Mor has a prolific show record in hand as well as under saddle. His most noted wins are male champion Royal Highland Show (RHS) in 2004 and Supreme RHS in 2006. He has several NPS Silver Medals culminating in winning the Kilmannan/NPS Silver Medal Final at Blair 2010. In 2009 he was a HOYS (Horse of The Year Show) finalist and in 2010 qualified for Olympia where he was awarded 'Best of Breed'. He is very well schooled and is very much a working stallion. His youngstock are now coming through in the show ring with notable success.

Moss-side Iain Mor

"First and foremost we treat all stallions as individuals. We believe in starting with them as foals and getting to know their specific personalities. Domhnach, which means Sunday in Gaelic, arrived a few days early on a Sunday morning with a 'where have you been' attitude. He's a real character, a fun pony that likes to do things his way. We work with him. Iain works with us. He is completely different. Iain's very laid back and takes his time when covering.

"It's important to take foals to shows. Ours get leading lessons at home and are introduced to the horsebox. They are manageable at this age and learn so much by going to a show. We continue handling our colts periodically through their early life, bringing them in several times a year for a week or so and quietly reminding them of their manners. The yearling colts get a spell out with Domhnach who is brilliant with them. He stands for no nonsense but is gentle. He has natural authority and they all respect that. Apart from being with Domhnach or sessions up at the yard, the young colts live out in a bachelor herd. We never show a colt from two years old onwards without a bridle and stallion roller. The equipment is designed to keep them off you and under control. It's a safety precaution that we consider essential. At two, the colts may cover a couple of mares. At three years old, they may get three or four selected mares. One of our young stallions trumpeted like an elephant when we introduced him to his first mare. He's never done it again and we haven't heard it since. It was an incredible sound.

"Our stallions are lightly backed for riding at three and a half years of age or four depending on how mature they are. The basic groundwork is done here before they go for training at a professional yard. They are schooled for about a month and may go to a winter show to be shown in hand if they are mature enough. After that they are turned away here for the winter. In the spring, as four-year-olds, they come back for more schooling. In the summer we try to get them shown in hand a couple of times and if they are ready, competing in one or two novice ridden classes. They progress in their own time depending on their mental attitude and how they mature. We like to vary their experiences to keep them fresh. When they are being shown or worked, stallions need to concentrate on their handler or rider. Talking to any other horses is strongly discouraged.

"The senior stallions live on their own mainly because they are too precious to risk. We turned a young stallion out with an old mare in our early days and it didn't go well. Colts don't know when to stop. They 'over cover' which has a negative effect on their fertility and can get kicked to bits. We did turn Domhnach out with a quiet mare recently but he let us know immediately that he wasn't happy. He didn't want a mare living in his paddock with him. Mares can be very aggressive.

"We don't feed the stallions much. Domhnach couldn't handle any hard food at all when he was young. They get hay or haylage in the winter. Domhnach gets a handful of feed balancer daily when he's covering. Iain Mor needs more during the breeding season and gets a small feed. It's a fine line - too little food and Iain lacks enthusiasm for his job; too much food and he can start to show some aggression that is so out of character.

56

"The stallions only get more hard feed when they are in serious competition mode and being ridden and worked every day. Domhnach lives out all winter and Iain used to! He started coming in when he was clipped and rugged for Olympia and somehow that regime has stuck. This year the aim is to get him back out in all weathers again like a proper Highland pony. We'll play it by ear.

"Both stallions cover in hand. Domhnach has his own rather unorthodox way. We bring a mare to Domhnach's field to try her over a wooden gate. If she is in season, we say 'away you go' and Domhnach walks himself off to a respectful distance. We then bring the mare into the field and position ourselves on the other side of the gate. We have to be fairly quick as Domhnach doesn't hang about when it comes to covering his mares. Once the job is done, we lead the mare out through the gate and Domhnach goes back to grazing. Iain is so much slower and more 'laid back'. He serves his mares in the covering yard just at the back of the house. This is where we started with him and established his routine.

"Dealing with stallions is a matter of listening to each individual and evaluating his reactions. We steer them out of any situation that could possibly lead to conflict or trouble. We had a grey mare one year that became very frightened when she was lead towards Iain Mor. She had been bullied by a black mare and was totally unable to relax in our black stallion's presence. It was a potentially dangerous situation so we stopped the proceedings straight away. Domhnach covered her without any stress or problem instead. Domhnach doesn't like mouse dun mares. He will cover them but isn't his normal enthusiastic self. We have no idea why. Every visiting mare has to be swabbed or treated with a course of antibiotics. Our own mares are treated with antibiotics once they have foaled. The stallions get a six to seven day course prior to covering and another half way through the breeding season as directed by our vet. This is a precaution against infection. All visiting mares are wormed as they arrive and spend their first twenty-four hours in a stable. Visiting mares get turned out together in a large paddock in front of the house where we can keep an eye on them. If there's a problem we remove the troublemaker. Iain's paddock is just over the drive so we can see when a mare starts taking an interest in him.

"Visiting mares are 'tried' with the stallion every second day. They usually stay here until they are scanned in foal. When people ask if they can bring a mare to one of our stallions, we always ask why they want a foal, what they want to do with them and if they have facilities for youngstock. There are too many horses and ponies in the country not being used and we feel it is important to only breed for the right reasons.

"We are often asked to advise people on which stallion to use. We assess the mare and try to match her up with the sire that will improve her weak points. Breeding should always be to improve on what you started with. We try and discourage people from using a neighbour's stallion just because it is handy. The Highland Pony Society offers a travel grant to members to encourage mare owners to travel and use the best stallion available. The society has also reintroduced a Premium Stallion Scheme. If the stallion gains enough points after assessment by five judges he will be awarded premium status. The aim is to help mare owners chose top class stallions. Sentimentality should never come in to breeding choices. We were delighted when Moss-side Iain Mor gained premium status. We have three young colts coming on in the wings. We assess all of our colts as yearlings and again as two-year-olds. We geld those at any stage that we feel are not coming up to the mark. Our breeding stock has to stand out and display true Highland pony quality. Our ultimate aim is to look to the future and promote the best of the Highland breed."

Willie with Moss-side Iain Mor

Charlie and Gina Parker
Dales Ponies

Charlie and
Wharfedale Prince Regent

A forester since 1971, Charlie Parker regularly uses his Dales ponies and Dales cobs for 'snigging' or timber extraction using horses/ponies. Gina has been involved with the breed since she was a child and enjoyed many days hunting on a Dales pony. At their Roandale stud they strive to breed ponies true to type with excellent temperaments, good bone and conformation.

Their present stallions are: **Roandale Bobby** (Dartdale Shamrock x Kilmond Jean, blue roan, 14 hh.) and **Roandale Socky Tom** (Colliery David x Hodgson Lane Finality, black,14.2 hh) was named after a famous border reiver.

"While we breed for type and performance and not colour. We are known for our rare, roan Dales ponies. We bought the bay roan stallion Wharfedale Prince Regent bred by Margaret Harvey when he was fifteen years old. This lovely stallion left us with an extremely rare bay roan line. We were also lucky enough to purchase a blue roan mare, Kilmond Jean, and she gave us the blue roan colour. If we hadn't bought these ponies the roan gene could well have died out in the breed. At the moment we have seven roan ponies. Roandale Bobby is the only blue roan stallion registered with the Dales Pony Society.

Charlie snigging with Lowkbers Bracken

"We broke Prince Regent to ride, drive and work in the forest. He took to the work like he had done it all his life. As a stallion, he whined a bit to a gelding also 'snigging' in the forest but Regent was a first class pony with a super temperament. Most of our brood mares are his daughters or granddaughters. When we first got Regent we were advised to get a brown Dales mare to better our chances of breeding roan foals. This mare's first four foals by Regent were a bay roan filly, a black colt, a blue roan colt and a bay filly. A lady with black mares who used Regent was lucky and got two roan foals. You never know what you will get with the roan gene.

"We also breed part bred Dales. We had two coloured vanner cob mares that we put to a Dales stallion. We felt the combination would provide a useful cob for forestry work and we were proved right. The cross produces a bigger, stronger cob ideal for heavier work. We have used our Dales cobs for riding, driving, harrowing and hay making as well as for snigging timber.

"As strong supporters of British Native ponies and being Yorkshire folk, it had to be Dales for us. It is such a versatile mountain and moorland breed, a true all-rounder and is hard to beat for forestry work.

"When Charlie started extracting timber twenty odd years ago, horses had virtually disappeared from the woods. Now they are seen as an environmentally friendly alternative to heavy machinery. Dales are reliable, very strong for their size and have admirable stamina. They soon learn what's required of them. Mostly the ponies are called in to thin plantations that are inaccessible to machinery. They can get into tight awkward places, they are manoeuvrable and can negotiate steep sided slopes. They leave little if any mess, cause no damage to the trees left in the wood and create no noise or air pollution. Timber extraction using horses/ponies is a viable, age-old skill that we strive to keep alive. We have developed special bonds with our ponies. When you are working alongside them day after day you get to know your animals very well. Quick to learn and willing to please, Dales thrive on varied work and enjoy a challenge. They are inspirational.

"Charlie often gives demonstrations of his horse logging work at shows and fêtes. When time allows he is able to offer tuition in the traditional skills of working ponies in chains and is happy to give advice to those seeking to work ponies on the land and particularly in forestry where his expertise lies."

Roandale mares and foal

Bert and Carole Morland
Fells Ponies

**Mares and foals on
Roundthwaite Common**

Bert and Carole Morland have both had life-long involvement with equines. Carole had great success as a trainer and driver of harness racing horses, including being British Ladies Grasstrack Champion. Her introduction to Fell ponies began when her father used some for trekking. Her interest grew after she married Bert who runs the semi-feral herd of Lunesdale ponies on valleys and hills of Roundthwaite Common, Tebay. Together they expanded the herd and bred and successfully rode, drove and showed the ponies. Carole and Bert have both written books about their beloved Fell ponies and spent countless hours observing the herd out on the fell. They are an authority on the qualities a British mountain and moorland pony needs to thrive in its native habitat. At present their stallions are:

Lunesdale Tarquin (50793C, 13.2.h.h. Lunesdale Mountain Mist x Lunesdale Helen). Tarquin is a super stamp of Fell pony that is leaving lovely stock. He was Reserve Champion at the 2005 Fell Pony Society Stallion Show.

Lunesdale Tarquin

Lunesdale Warlord (71091C, 13.2 hh. Greenholme Warrior x Lunesdale Lady Rebecca). Warlord is a very traditional pony with great conformation, bone, action and temperament. He has been retained for his quality but also his bloodlines compliment many of the Lunesdale mares. He's had great success in the show ring including being supreme champion at the Fell Pony Society's Stallion Show.

Lunesdale Warlord

"Cumbria's Fell ponies are one of Britain's rare and less known mountain and moorland breeds. They are very special and a national heritage. At the Lunesdale Stud we endeavour to produce Fell ponies that are true to type and able to exist on their native heath. Our objective has always been to retain natural characteristics and hardiness and at the same time breed useful ponies that can excel as working, driving and riding animals. There is little call now for Fells to do farm work but some still do an excellent job 'log snigging' for foresters. Recently Fells have been used to carry loads to repair footpaths in the high mountains of the Lake District. Stallions are as capable as mares or geldings for this. Mostly however, today's Fell pony stallions are used for studwork, in hand or ridden showing and private driving.

"Ideally we like them to be up to the old maximum height of 13.2 hands rather than the new height of 14 hands. The traditional, smaller ponies are better able to thrive on their native fells than larger ponies. Conformation is a priority as is good all round movement. They should have a well laid back shoulder, good hooves, ground covering trot, flat bone and plenty of straight silky feather. The Lunesdale ponies have been successful in different disciplines. Fells have tremendous versatility. The grey stallion, Lunesdale Mountain Mist, is a good example. After studwork at Lunesdale, he was exported to the Czech Republic. In addition to covering mares he has embarked on a whole new lifestyle that includes western style barrel racing, driving and show jumping. He just goes to prove how able and willing these fantastic Fell ponies are!

Lunesdale Mountain Mist

"The Lunesdale Fell pony stud was formed in the 1950s. The first stallion used was called Heltondale Sonny Boy. He was unbroken, extremely wild and quite difficult to break in. But once he was handled, we used him extensively for shepherding. Those were the days before anyone had a quad bike! Sonny Boy was a good type and he won the Fell Pony Society Stallion Show championship in the 1960s.

"The next stallion we used quite prolifically during the 1970s was the grey Mountain Flash II. One of his colts, Lunesdale Lucky Jim, covered mares for many years at the Sleddale Fell Stud. Another of his sons, the well-known Lunesdale Jerry, was to shape the future of the Lunesdale Stud. He was also probably one of the most influential and prolific stallions in the Fell Pony Society from the 1970s until the early 1990s. After stud duties at Lunesdale, he went on to stand at the Townend and then the Castle Hill Stud. He lived to a great age.

Lunesdale Henry

"Jerry left behind a fantastic heritage. His son, Lunesdale Henry, sired many in hand, ridden, dressage and driving champions. These include Lunesdale Rebecca (three times Breed Show Supreme Champion), Lunesdale Evening Star (Breed Show Supreme Champion and Olympia Ridden qualifier), Lunesdale Prince Henry (dressage & driven champion) and Lunesdale Mountain Mist (Supreme In Hand Champion at the Austrian Horse of the Year Show). One of Henry's great, great grandsons, Lunesdale Warlord, is our present stud stallion. This year, we are hoping that he will make his mark in ridden show ring classes.

"To survive out on the fell, the ponies need to be quick-witted, intelligent and curious. Fell stallions, in our experience, have an exemplary temperament. Those that don't are usually the product of human mismanagement. They thrive on reward and activity that engages and challenges them.

"It's been fascinating to watch the stallions in their mating rituals. Apart from scenting the mare's urine and sniffing the air, the stallions perform a 'courtship dance'. With his tail lifted and neck arched, the stallion high steps in front of the mare trying to impress her. The stallions know how to interpret the mare's response. If she is not ready to mate, he will go back to grazing but keep her within his sights. The ritual will be repeated until the mare is fully in season and accepts the stallion's advances. Sometimes a stallion takes a dislike to a mare and shows no interest in her even when she is obviously in season. Some stallions have favourites. If one of these is in season, he may cover her frequently while ignoring another also showing oestrus. On occasion a dominant mare will try to prevent the stallion mating with others by herding and guarding him. She may succeed with a young stallion but an older, experienced sire will usually retaliate and put her in her place.

"There is a hierarchy that governs the running of a herd, each animal having a set position behind a leader - normally, but not always, the stallion. We don't run stallions on the open fell as public bridleways cross the land. Instead we 'gather' the mares, herding them in family groups by quad bike off the fell before they are due to foal. Those we want to breed will either run with the stallion on an enclosed piece of fell,called an allotment, or are covered in hand. We mostly keep our female lines and buy in fresh blood via stallions, but have bought mares from time to time from other hill studs.

"The Lunesdale herd is mainly black with one or two browns and greys. Brown and bay is seen less today as many of the bloodlines carrying those colour genes were presumed lost or at least diluted when black became more fashionable. There are definitely more greys now than twenty years ago. We breed for quality. Colour is secondary. Our grey stallion, Lunesdale Tarquin, has been retained as he is a lovely, traditional pony. Tarquin is now breeding show-winning stock.

"We are so extremely lucky to have been able to spend so much time observing ponies living as a herd in their native landscape and gain an understanding and knowledge of their natural behaviour. To go up the fell on a peaceful summer's evening and watch the foals playing and the mares grooming each other, in such spectacular scenery, is an almost indescribable pleasure and privilege. We hope to inspire future generations to keep these herds that are so vital to our national breeding stock, out on the fell where they belong."

Lunesdale colts in the Cumbrian Hills

Jackie Webb
Connemara Ponies

Bunowen Castle Ri

Only two ponies have won the NPS/Baileys Horse Feeds Supreme Ridden Mountain and Moorland Championship twice and they have both been Connemaras. The first was Rosenharley Rossleague in 1984. It was thought unlikely that a pony would ever achieve such great showing heights again but in 2007, **Bunowen Castle Ri** (S001122, Village Boy CPS 927 x Dame Bunowen Castle Queen CPS 9548), Jackie Webb's Connemara stallion, proved the skeptics wrong. He is a great ambassador for his breed.

"I first came across Connemara ponies when I was a child. I was show jumping mad and liked Connies as they came from Ireland and were well known for their performance and ability. I wasn't interested then on their conformation or looks, just their jumping prowess. Ever since then though, performance has remained in the forefront of my breeding aims.

"I started Blackthorn Stud in 1974 with thoroughbreds and breeding Exmoors in 1978. I was lucky enough to have the Exmoor stallion Siskin who was a prolific winner in hand and under saddle.

"I rekindled an interest in Connies when I was showing Exmoors. Connemaras always fascinated me. Their calm but alert attitude, true pony quality and exceptional movement became a magnet. I started visiting studs in England and Ireland, qualified as a NPS Mixed Mountain & Moorland judge and eventually joined the Connemara judging panel. At this stage I decided it was time to start breeding Connemaras.

"My first mares went away to stud but in time, the decision was made to have my own stallion. With the help of well-respected Connemara enthusiast, Sarah Hodgkins, the yearling colt, Lough Fee Warrior, came to join us. He was a great character with a superb pony head and temperament second to none. He proved himself to be a first class performance stallion, earning his ridden stallion premium.

"When Sarah came back from Ireland some years later with a collection of Connemara colts to bring on, she invited me to come and look them over. One colt stood out for me. He was gangling and rangy but he had something – that 'look at me' quality. He became known as 'Jackie's Boy'. Through the following winter the colts played and galloped and ploughed their field into a quagmire. Sarah decided they had to be sold on and rang me. I didn't want or need a colt. I had Warrior and he was breeding lovely offspring but there was something about 'Jackie's Boy' that I just couldn't turn down. It turned out to be the best decision of my life.

"So Bunowen Castle Ri came into my life as a yearling. He was so rangy that I left him to grow on until he was three. Only then did I put him forward for grading. He passed with flying colours. That year he covered his first mares and Matthew Lawrence took him on to show. Ri was really naughty that first season, showing off to the girls and paying little attention to anything else. To overcome the problem Matthew took Ri to lots of local shows where he just walked him round the show ground and the collecting ring. Eventually Ri got bored, gave up his antics and by the end of that season Matthew was able to show him. First time out Ri took the championship!

"Matthew backed him as a four year old and showed him under saddle at five. We had something special and Ri proved us right by being unbeaten in Novice Ridden Mountain and Moorland classes.

"At six years old, Ri qualified for Olympia on his first attempt - if fact throughout his showing career he always qualified on his first attempt for the big shows. He won consistently including the In Hand BCPS Breed Championship three times. In 2007 he won both In Hand and Ridden BCPS Supreme Championships. He took Supreme at HOYS that same year and was also awarded his greatest victory by winning Olympia for the second time.

"Ri made Matthew's name and Matthew has said of him 'He's a total star. For four years, he's come here and he's tried his best. One can't ask any more. He's exceptional, and I owe it all to him.'

Matthew and Ri at Olympia

"I used Ri every year to cover my mares, even during his showing years. He has bred some outstanding stock, all inheriting his lovely temperament, pony characteristics and most importantly, now that they are 'coming of age', their ability to perform under saddle. I have a daughter of Ri's waiting in the wings to show next year. We have great hopes for her.

70

"After winning Olympia twice, Ri retired and is now my stud stallion. Warrior fractured a leg but he completely recovered. He went on to a lovely breeding home in France. He's still there. Ri runs with my mares during the breeding season and we cover outside mares in hand. The rest of the year he lives in his own field next to the mares. He is a pony of a lifetime and my idea of near perfection in his breed. He has not let me down. Who can ask more than that?"

Haselor Cormack by Bunowen Castle Ri

Len and Ann Bigley
Welsh Cobs

**Len Bigley with
Llanarth Prince
of Wales**

Len and Ann run the well-known Llanarth Stud in the foot of the Black Mountains with their children Simon and Catryn. They currently have four Welsh Cob stallions, two Welsh section Bs and a part bred riding pony stallion who is Welsh B x Arab/ Thoroughbred. It is the Welsh Cobs that the Bigleys and the Llanarth Stud are best known for.

"The 1970s were halcyon years for the Llanarth Stud with Welsh Cob stallions like Llanarth Flying Comet and Llanarth Meredith being virtually unbeaten in the show ring. Both stallions won cob but also mixed mountain and moorland classes and that was a special accolade for us. Both Comet and Meredith qualified four times for the Breeders In Hand Championship at HOYS. Comet was also 'Pony of the Year' four times and Overall Supreme twice. In many ways these two stallions set the stage for the success that was to follow in later years for Welsh Cobs.

"Llanarth Lloyd George was another notable stallion. He was a superb stamp and supreme champion at Ponies UK. Sold to the Sydenham Stud, he sired a generation of ponies that did much to make the performance Cobs that we see today. Llanarth British Lion was exceptional too. He qualified for Olympia and HOYS for both Ridden and In Hand Championships in the same year. He is now in retirement at stud and grazing on the veldt in South Africa.

"As a policy, we diligently keep our female lines and have never been afraid to use other stallions. We were fortunate to have Crugybar Mabon Mai here as a youngster for four years. He 'clicked' well with our mares. We have a generation of lovely offspring by Mabon including our senior stallion, **Llanarth Prince of Wales** (Crugybar Mabin Mai x LlanarthNellie). Prince is proving to be a great stock-getter, like his sire, and has been increasingly popular as a stud stallion.

Len and Llanarth Old Fashion

"We had Menai Sparkling Magic on loan from Germany for four years. He sired our young stallions **Llanarth Seldom Seen** (Menai Sparkling Magic x Llanarth Norma Jean) and **Llanarth Fiery Jack** (Menai Sparkling Magic x Llanarth Pam Evans). They have already made their mark in the show ring both in hand and under saddle and we are really encouraged by their progress and success. More importantly for us, their first foals are very promising. Our latest purchase is **Penllangrug Deio** (Thornyside The Terminator x Caerllwyn Princess Dawn) whose dam we really like. We bought Deio as a two-year-old to outcross to our mare line. He is already producing beautiful progeny with our mares. One of his first colt foals was exported to Australia last year.

"We like traditional Welsh Cobs with good pony characteristics. Our Cobs tend to stand around 14.2 to 15 hands. Any bigger and they can loose essential pony qualities. They must have a 'leg at each corner', plenty of bone, straight movement and all important, a super temperament. We have too many ponies to keep a worrier or challenging stallion. It's not what we would want to breed from anyway. We treat the stallions like normal ponies and train them to behave with respect to their handler at all times. They all have a special covering bridle, usually a straight bar bit, so they know when they are covering and when they are not. We are patient with the stallions but they must understand that it is their handler that is always in control. They start covering a couple of mares at the age of two. It's then that we teach them manners and to approach a mare calmly, quietly and cautiously. We want them to tease a mare properly and never rush the job.

"The stallions are stabled during 'the season' next door to each other, travel together to shows and get on well. In the autumn they get turned out together with the colts. We're never had any fighting or injury. The mares all go away to winter grazing to rest our fields, so there are no distractions over the winter for the stallions.

Llanarth Seldom Seen

"In the spring, we often run one stallion out with the mares we have chosen for him that season. He won't be shown that year and runs with about ten mares.

"They all come in at the end of winter. The stallions are all broken to ride and are usually ridden several times a week. They get as much turn out as possible every day whatever the weather. When they are in, they are fed hay and haylage.

During the showing and covering season, they get a small feed of sugar beet pulp and pony mix twice a day. We don't use supplements or calmers. If a stallion needed the later, he wouldn't stay. Each stallion covers between twenty-five and forty-five mares a year. Visiting mares usually get turned out in small groups. We don't turn out barren mares in the same field as mares with foals.

"The stallions often cover a mare the morning of a show. It doesn't make any difference. They know when they are tacked up with a showing or riding bridle that they won't be covering. All of our stallions are broken to ride. We use snaffles when they are young and a double bridle once they qualify for open classes. They are trained through long reining, to balance themselves when working in hand. Only when they are really well balanced and using their hocks properly, do we gradually start to teach them to extend their paces. It takes a while for them to learn to perform correctly the famous Welsh Cob extended trot.

"The stud is very much a family concern. From a young age, Catryn and Simon have been interested in the breeding, riding and showing. It is the breeding that is so interesting and important to us. We always say that showing is the icing on the cake. But if the taste of success is sweet, our fantastic ponies have taken us to the top of a sugar mountain."

Simon and Llanarth Prince of Wales

India Latter
Welsh Mountain Ponies

**India and
Powys Sprite**

India lives in Carmarthenshire, looks after, rides and shows two Welsh stallions. She owns Section A, eight year old, **Powys Sprite** (Heniarth Quinnell x Lacy Sable) and produces sixteen year old, Section B, **Blaenpentre Silver Coin** (Llangeitho Sovereign x Cusop Sunset) for his owners. India has qualified for HOYS ten times and Olympia on three occasions.

"I began riding stallions for other people at the age of twelve, which is the minimum required rider age for competing an entire in the ring. I was asked to ride the Section A stallions Heniarth Quip and Heniarth Mr Milligan for the Heniarth stud, and the Section B stallion Rhoson Shem for the Rhoson Stud. They were all fabulous stallions. I learnt then a lot about the basic temperaments of the stallions, how they should be treated, handled, trained and ridden. I prefer to compete on stallions as they have that 'extra something'. Most of them are real showmen, and if treated correctly they are more than happy to show off their amazing presence.

India and Blaenpentre Silver Coin

"As I am petite, I have been able to continue riding Welsh A and B stallions as an adult. I get to know each as an individual so I can understand them and keep them out of trouble. Heniarth Quinnell (Sprite's sire) was the first stallion on my yard. He arrived in 2006 and finished 3rd at HOYS in 2008. Blaenpentre Silver Coin, known as Dufus and owned by the Mead Family, came to us by chance really. My Mum loaned her Welsh Cob mare to the Meads. When she dropped the mare off, she saw Dufus in the field and brought him home!! I think it was love at first sight. He moved so well and was a real poser and was wasted doing nothing in the field so she thought he would be a lovely pony for me to show.

"Stabling arrangements have been shuffled around a bit to accommodate the stallions but we treat them as ponies. We respect their individual needs and they have been no problem at all.

"Dufus is a tense, sensitive pony so we gave him time to settle. During his first couple of seasons, we showed him lightly at local and county level. Only when he relaxed did we step up to competing him at top class level. He was Novice Ridden Champion at the National Welsh show in 2007, National Open Ridden Champion at the National Welsh Championship Show in 2008 and first qualified for HOYS in 2009. He's an excitable pony and quite a difficult ride. I was worried how he would cope and perform in the atmosphere at HOYS. He took it all in his stride, really enjoyed showing off and was second in the Ridden Mountain and Moorland Welsh Section A and B final. At the time it was an achievement beyond my wildest dreams. Dufus went home to the Meads' Blaenpentre stud for a break and covering duties. Dufus never covers and shows under saddle in the same season. He just can't handle doing both jobs at the same time. When he covers, he runs out with the mares as well as covering in hand. He's never covered at our yard as I like to keep it all separate. When he's here with me, he knows that he's here to work and not to impress the ladies! I've shown him in hand a couple of times. He's been champion on each occasion but it's hard work running alongside him. He's such an extravagant mover that I struggle to keep up.

"Dufus won two championships last year including the supreme champion that qualified him for HOYS at NPS Area 25. Over-showing can make ponies switch off. Dufus loves performing and is an exuberant character but he does usually settle and behave. As soon as he's had enough of the show ring though, he starts being naughty. We then know that he needs time out and a break from it all.

"At the end of 2011, I sold my Connemara gelding and literally within minutes of him leaving, I had an email to say that a pony I'd been trying to buy for five years was for sale. This was Powys Sprite who we affectionately call Super Sprite at home. I saw him in a photo as a yearling and knew he was special. I had to wait until he was five before he came up for sale. We bought him without hesitation.

"Sprite was well handled when he arrived so I broke him in over that winter and brought him on slowly in preparation for his showing career. During his first season under saddle he only had eight outings but either won or was champion on most of his outings and he qualified for HOYS. We hoped Sprite was capable of winning his section of the Picton final at the NPS finals and follow in the footsteps of his uncle, Heniarth Quip, who won in 2003. Sprite obviously had bigger plans. He not only won but went on to be Supreme Picton Final Champion. To our delight Sprite also won overall champion of the Mountain and Moorland Working Hunter Pony Leyhills Starter Stakes final - not bad for our third time around a course of jumps! He loves jumping. It's a change from ridden showing and helps keep him enthusiastic. This year he won at the Royal Welsh beating his sire Heniarth Quinnell and was awarded the Velvet Cup for best ridden Section A. We had an amazing time at the WPCS performance show where Sprite won the dressage, the show jumping, cross country, ridden showing, hunter trials and open hunter classes. He won seven cups, four sashes and loads of rosettes over the two days. He is such a happy and willing pony who we are immensely proud of - a definite superstar.

India and Powys Sprite

"Due to lack of grazing, the stallions don't get much permanent turn out but cope well. We have had stallions we could turn out with geldings but Sprite and Dufus both think they are the best ponies in the world. They would bully the geldings, so go out alone - better to be safe than sorry. They like to roll in their beds every time you move even a flake of shavings. They are easy to muck out though as all their droppings are in one place. I don't find stallions any more difficult than mares or geldings. You have to be more aware of them but I would honestly trust 'the boys' at home in their stables with a child. They are brilliant.

"They go out most days, come rain or shine. Sometimes it's ridden work or it could be a play in a paddock. Some days they will do a hard eight-mile hack with little walking. Other days they do a forty-five minute walk around the block or they get twenty minutes cantering and playing in the hayfields. When they are showing, I have a lesson once a week so they each get an hour every fortnight. They really have to pull their socks up and work hard. In the winter the stallions go hunting. They love it and it's a complete break from the control and pressure of showing. There is a risk they could get hurt but they could do that cantering round their field or getting cast in their stable.

"I treat the 'boys' as I would any other show pony. They are lightly rugged in the summer and then clipped and heavily rugged during the winter. They work year round, and as they hunt, they're clipped out in the winter. I don't tend to feed hard feed throughout the summer. They get fed on good quality ad lib haylage and don't need any extra. I feed once a day in winter at about six pm. They get chaff, or ready grass, with a little mix and sugar beet. When Dufus was younger he was a terrible eater and we fed him four times a day. He doesn't fret so much now and keeps weight on better. It really does depend on the pony.

"Sprite doesn't have any calmer for the shows. He's a little 'squealy' but I work him through that. Dufus tends to be fed a herbal calmer for a couple of weeks before a bigger show. We find it works really well with him and just takes the edge off any over exuberance. He has so much presence in the ring that he could never be too calm.

"Showing a stallion has its challenges but the most important consideration is to be aware of the other ponies around you in (and outside) of the ring. Sometimes another pony, a mare in season, can distract a stallion. Then it is my job to get him focused and move him away from that other pony to avoid a potential problem. It's important to give a stallion his own space. My 'boys' are schooled to do leg yield, shoulder in, etc. I use these exercises to get their focus back on me.

"When I am showing, my mum is a great ally. While I am preparing the stallions and working them in, she scouts the scene. She then gives me the heads up on any ponies displaying high spirits or mares in season. I then know which ponies to stay away from – it's a real team effort.

"I have a very flexible job and fit the ponies in around my hours. I usually work three days and two evenings a week. I'm lucky that in the summer I can fit my shifts around the shows.

"Long term we plan to use Sprite for Artifical Insemination breeding. I don't really want him covering at home. We don't have the facilities for visiting mares and I want to keep this yard as his place of work. Dufus is sixteen years old and has retired to stud at Blaenpentre where he was born. That is a perfect and fitting retirement for such a champion pony.

"I think mainly because of my size, Welsh ponies have chosen me. They are full of character and cheeky chappies so need small but capable jockeys. When I'm on a little Welshie I feel completely within my comfort zone. They are what I know and love. I've had different ponies but always go back to my Welsh boys!"

Dufus, India and Sprite

Robert Maton
New Forest Ponies

Knavesash
Knight

New Forest ponies run in the Maton family blood. Robert has owned, bred and ridden these beautiful ponies since he was a boy. His brother has three stallions and his children breed them under their own prefixes. His son inherited the Woodfidley prefix from his step-great grandmother and his daughter the Furzey Lodge prefix with her great grandfather. Robert now runs the Mallards Wood Stud with his wife near Beaulieu. They have a carefully chosen mix of stud and forest bred New Forest ponies including two stallions and a yearling colt:

Mallards Wood Magician (2010 bay roan,S52/167, Applewitch Pure Magic x Mallards Wood Goddess).

Knavesash Knight (2010 black,S52/168,Willoway Minstral x Sunnydale Delight).

Mallards Wood Apollo (2012 bay colt, Willoway Minstral x Mallards Wood Delphi).

Robert Maton and Mallards Wood Goddess

The Mallards Wood New Forest Pony Stud has a carefully integrated mix of stud and forest bloodlines producing show-winning ponies at county level. Robert breeds for temperament as well as correct confirmation and performance. His encyclopaedic knowledge of the area of the forest that he works in, and every one of the six hundred ponies in it, earns him great respect.

"Ponies have roamed the New Forest since the end of the last Ice Age and they shape the landscape here. Without them the forest would be more overgrown with less variety of wildlife. At the moment there are over five thousand ponies running on the forest, of which a considerable number are purebred New Forest ponies.

"Registered New Foresters that are sired, born and reared until weaning on the open forest are termed as being 'forest bred'. All forest bred foals are sired by approved registered stallions that are selected for type, temperament, conformation and pedigree. These ponies are often sold at a reasonable price at the annual sales and can turn out to be real gems. We enthusiasts say a forest pony has the loveliest nature of all the native breeds. They are usually easy to break-in and handle.

"Since 1994, I have been employed by the New Forest Verderers as one of their five Agisters. Agisters are selected by Verderers who form a council that is selected by Commoners or appointed as representatives of the crown, government departments and county council. Each Agister has an allocated region of the forest in which to oversee the management and welfare of the commoners' stock living in that area. My section is one of the southern areas. All the ponies that wander freely over the 37,500 hectares of open forest are owned by people who have 'Rights of Common of Pasture'. About four hundred commoners use their right and there is no limit to the number of ponies they can turn out.

"Once over a hundred stallions roamed the forest living out all year. The fact that this year only ten stallions ran out on the forest at the beginning of May, and only for a month, is a clear sign of the times. Next year we expect around two hundred and fifty forest bred foals. Last year about two hundred and fifty were sold, so numbers are staying level. We don't want the population to drop much as the breed is only one stage away from being listed as a 'rare breed'. The market for forest-bred young stock has fallen dramatically. Even though visitors like to see foals, and we need to conserve the breed, the low demand for forest-bred youngsters has lead to a concerned rethink of breeding policy. The aim now is not only to reduce the numbers of foals born each year but also to select top quality stallions to improve the quality and saleability of their offspring. Only the crème de la crème are chosen. The ponies' bloodlines are important and carefully studied. A stallion will not be turned out onto the same area for more than three years to ensure he does not breed with his own offspring.

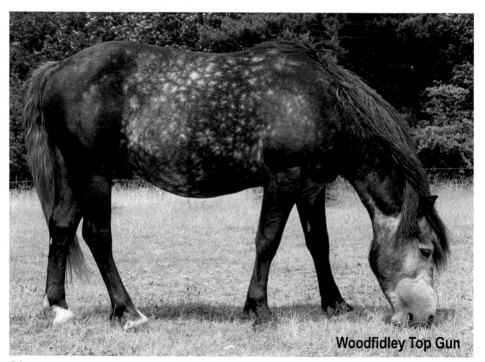
Woodfidley Top Gun

"One of my tasks as an Agister is to supervise the stallions in my area, especially when they are first turned out. Some of the mares are only ever handled when they are branded, yet they are almost never aggressive to people. Go down to Hatchet Pond on a summer's day and there will be families sitting on the ground having picnics, mums pushing babies in push chairs, ice cream vans, dogs off the lead and ponies everywhere coming in for a drink. The fact we have so few problems is largely due to the kind and intelligent nature of the breed.

New Forest ponies at Hatchet Pond

"When the stallions are turned out, many of the local riders sensibly avoid the areas where the entires are running. Occasionally a stallion wanders out of his allotted area. If this happens, the Agister will help the owner to find, catch and return him to where he is supposed to be.

"One and two year old fillies run out on the forest with their dam and the stallions but they are rarely covered until they are four years old or older. Forage is short in the forest and the ponies mature very slowly. We also have yearling colts still running on their dams. Again due to immaturity and slow development they don't cover mares that come into season late in the year. We know this as we get very few late foals the following year. By the first of February of a colt's second year, his owners must geld or remove him from the forest. Donkey stallions though are allowed to roam freely all year. As long as the donkeys are raised with their own kind, they think they are donkeys and don't breed with the ponies. It's very unusual to get a mule born here.

"When the stallions' month on the forest is up, the Agisters help to round them up and return them to the stallion enclosures.

"There are twenty-five mature stallions all living together in the 'stallion field' and a few up and coming youngsters in an adjacent area. They live together amicably with little to no fighting. In the absence of mares, they establish a hierarchy amongst themselves and tend to wander off in pairs or small groups. Right now for example we have a seventeen year old stallion who is best mates with a five-year-old. There is plenty of space so individuals that don't get on so well can avoid each other and stay out of trouble.

"Even though only ten stallions went out this year, we keep a much higher number to maintain a healthy gene pool for the Verderers to choose from. A stallion may not be used for several years but then be turned out to cover another stallion's offspring. Once a stallion is over eighteen years old he is no longer in the Verderers' stallion scheme and his owner will be asked to collect him. Some continue to be used in pony studs, while others are gelded. I break all my stallions at four for ridden work so they are prepared for anything later in life. My good stallion Mallards Wood Gigolo (Monkshorn Trooper x Brookshill Juno) ran on the forest between the ages of two and eleven. He was then cut and went on to be a super ridden pony in a lovely home.

"As a family we have had great success with our stud and forest bred ponies. My best mare is Mallards Wood Goddess who was forest bred. She was three times Reserve Supreme Champion at the Breed Show, took Forest Bred Champion and supreme honours twice at the NFPEC Show and was Forest Bred Champion five times at the New Forest Show. She's proving to be a superb brood mare and has had seven foals from five different stallions. Her offspring are outstanding winning many championships and qualifying for HOYS and Olympia. Goddess is a great ambassador for the forest bred ponies.

"I enjoy showing my ponies at the highest level and I am determined to show that forest bred ponies do compete and win. I love my work. There's nowhere I would rather be. The forest is where I feel most at home."

Robert Maton is a free spirit like the ponies he watches over.

New Forest mares and youngsters

Oke Dene Red Alert

Jackie Ablett and Gill Langdon
Exmoor Ponies

Exmoor herd on Dunkery

Sisters Gill and Jackie run the Exmoor Pony Herd H17 (Tawbitts breeding herd) on Dunkery. They have about seventy registered ponies running out on approximately one hundred acres of enclosed moorland, fifty acres of unimproved pasture and a hundred and fifty acres of conservation grazing land.

"Many of our ponies are born and die out on Exmoor, coming in only to be halter broken and branded as youngsters. Most get no wormers, no foot care and only in the harshest winters do they need extra hay. They live like the wild ponies of the region from years past. The fact that they thrive out in their natural habitat is testament to their incredible hardy constitution and ancient lineage.

"The first Exmoor in our lives was a gelding called Nobby. He belonged to our Mother who drove him in a governess cart around Southend. He was her main form of transport during the war. Our family moved from Essex to Exmoor after the Second World War in the 1950s. Like many girls, we were really keen to have ponies but for us not any old pony; it had to be an Exmoor. Gill saved up and bought her first Exmoor, Puck, when she was eighteen. He had been found on Exford Common as an orphan and had been reared on goats' milk. Jackie got an Exmoor as a wedding present. That shows just how passionate we were about the breed.

"Our foundation mare was Hawkwell Lady Margaret. She was also a fosterling as her dam had broken a leg when Lady Margaret was only three weeks old. She survived by pinching milk off another mare and as a result was always small. She came to us as a two-year-old in 1972 but looked like a yearling. They say small is beautiful and so it proved with this pony. From the age of four she was never out of the ribbons. She was even Bath and West Champion at the age of twenty-one. She bred fourteen foals and lived into her thirties.

"Since starting Herd 17, we have bred many successful stallions and most have been memorable characters. Tawbitts Victor is one that comes to mind. He was a September foal and was brought off Dunkery at the 2005 gathering with all the other youngsters. As he was a late foal we overwintered him down on the Tawbitts holding. The following spring his life took an unexpected turn. A local donkey that had performed for years as palm-bearer at a nearby church unexpectedly died and Victor was commandeered to replace him. It was a last minute and unlikely role for a purebred, hill-born Exmoor but Victor behaved like he had been a regular attendant at Sunday worship. He took it all, bells, organ, choir and men in robes, in his stride. After his performance he trimmed back the churchyard grass, sparing the primroses, and enjoyed all the fuss from the congregation. The general verdict was that though his ears were a trifle short, he was otherwise 'very creditable!' And so an established tradition took on a unique turn. A new candidate for palm bearer is chosen annually from among the Tawbitts under twelve month crop of colts.

"At two, Victor went out as a Moor stallion. As he was well handled, he was very friendly – a bit too friendly! He started rounding up point to pointers being exercised on the moor and eventually he was deemed a problem for local riders. We brought him down from the moor after only two seasons and gelded him. He went on to be an in hand champion at the Bath and West Show and is now embarking on a ridden career. It was a shame he was cut as he left some lovely foals. Fortunately we have two of Victor's full brothers – Vulcan and Viceroy. The ponies are named after an original mare, so all the 'Vs' are 'Victoria's line'. Tawbitts Donald is from Damsel's line, Tawbiits Merlin from the 'Mystic line' and so on.

"Tawbits Young Mickey, Hawkwell Lady Margaret's last foal, ran with various herds of mares on the open moor first as a two year old and was retired at twelve. He managed to sire some extra foals without our knowing. Wild deer can put holes in fences or break a top strand. Although the fences are checked frequently, Mickey proved clever at getting into places he shouldn't have been - and then back again! We only found out about his escapades as all Exmoor foals are DNA tested. After retiring, Mickey was broken in a week, led through a village with a brass band playing and then shown in an indoor arena. He didn't bat an eyelid at any of it and behaved like a perfect gentleman. Mickey and Victor are great ambassadors for the Exmoor ponies and show just how amazing the breed's temperament is.

"At the moment we have senior stallions, **Tawbitts Lanzulot** (Coedywern Zulu x Tawbitts Tabitha) and **Tawbitts Golden Treacle** (Ebony x Golden Toffee)**,** running out on the moor with our two herds of mares. Four year old Tawbitts Merlin, is about to start his showing career. We have great hopes for him as the Mystic line has done really well in the show ring. Several have shown at HOYS. Then there's Tawbitts Donald who passed his stallion grading inspection last year.

Tawbitts Donald

"Exmoor ponies are popular for conservation grazing stock. We have loaned out colts for this purpose. It's a win-win situation. We can run the youngsters on and judge them for stallion potential after they have matured a little and at the same time they happily do their bit for conservation. We have even sold colts to France where they use them to graze down stretches of land that serve as fire breaks.

"We bring all our stallions on slowly. We do not feed them concentrates and let them mature as nature intended. Tawbitts Mystic Major started showing at nine and reached the peak of his success in his twelfth and thirteenth year. We never sell any of our stallions but we loan them out to good homes. That way we always know what happens to them and can ensure they have a useful and happy life. When a moor stallion's breeding career comes to an end, we do consider gelding them if appropriate to the individual pony. Many of 'our boys' have then gone on to enjoy riding activities successfully into an old age.

Tawbitts Euan

"Retirement does not feature in our plans – and that applies to us as well as ponies! Exmoors win you over and enrich your life beyond compare. We wouldn't want to be without them. During the last War, Exmoors were poached for meat and used as living targets by American gunners until there were only about fifty left.

"Today the breed is still endangered but hopefully we have helped to promote and increase the numbers of a pony that is a natural heritage. We came close to losing them and that can never be allowed to happen again."

Tough, totally enchanting and versatile, the Exmoor pony could have no better guardians than these two tough, enchanting and determined Exmoor ladies.

Julie Barton
Dartmoor Ponies

Julie with Moortown Honeyman

Julie is a professional producer of native ponies to show in hand and under saddle. Her yard is in Suffolk near Ipswich. A wide variety of natives comes into her busy yard year round to be broken, schooled or prepared for the show ring.

"I used to work with and ride horses but had to have an operation on my back that put paid to my riding career. At around that time I bought a half share in a Dartmoor gelding called Catalan Pablo with a friend. We started showing him and I got the bug. I work with several native breeds but Dartmoors hold a special place and it's the breed I am most involved with.

"I decided that if I was going to dedicate my equine career to showing, I wanted to get to the top. I did a lot of research and I bought Dartmoor gelding Hopelaws Flamingo. I showed him in hand, in ridden and working hunter classes and he was very successful. He was the first Dartmoor to win at HOYS and then he won there three times.

"The first stallion in my yard was Shilstone Rocks Snowfox. I was asked by his breeders to produce and show him to promote their well-known stud in Devon. After his first season, I bought Snowfox in partnership with the girl who rode him. He won numerous championships, was reserve overall ridden at HOYS and best of breed twice at Olympia. My co-owner bought him outright when he was ten.

"Next came Hisley Saunter who was a four year old stallion that I produced for his owners for a couple of seasons. I also bought him and he was champion more times than I can remember- a great pony. I gelded him as an eight-year-old for my nine year old daughter to show and he did her proud.

"I also had Shilstone Rocks War Lord, Snowfox's brother, for a couple of years and he too was a prolific winner. Then I bought my most successful Dartmoor stallion to date, Moortown Honeyman. He is really special because he is so multi-talented. He's been champion in hand, under saddle and as a working hunter pony. He has superb conformation, exceptional bone and is athletic as well.

"Most of the ponies are broken in the autumn of their third year. They learn the basics over six to eight weeks. They then go out for winter and come back in for light showing as a four-year-old. At five we start to ask more of them.

Hixton Honeyboy

"The stallions are fed ad lib haylage and only get hard feed and supplements if and when they need it. In January they come in and get rugged. I aim to get their winter coats out by March. Stallions can get fat necks and we usually get rid of these with correct work. If that's not enough, we use neck covers to sweat off the fat. I use loose ring Neue Schule snaffle bits with a lozenge to start the ponies and then go onto a Pelham or double bridle when they are mature. All the ponies get worked every other day either schooling or hacking and they all get turn out. We swap them around. Sometimes they get half a day and at other times all night in a paddock.

"My stallions are all produced for the show ring and most don't cover mares until they have finished their showing career. This stops them losing condition and keeps their mind concentrating on their showing job. They learn they are going out to perform in the ring and what's expected of them. This way I don't have stallions shrieking at mares in the yard or showground. It enables me to travel entires with mares to a show and tie them up calmly outside the box. I don't put stallions and mares right next to each other but they can see each other. They also all hack out together and with mares. I don't really treat stallions that differently.

"I turn out almost all of the geldings, colts and young stallions (except those qualified for Olympia) together in October when HOYS is over onto a nineteen-acre field. They start doing this as weaned foals and learn the hierarchy. I do keep a close watch especially if they are clients' ponies but I haven't ever had any fighting. Stallions can live out together, if they are used to the regime from a young age and there are no mares nearby. They have four months quality chill out time. Honeyman spent his early years out with a pony called Moortown Countryman. Countryman came to me as an eight year old to be broken after several years as a stud pony. He instantly recognized Honeyman and they became inseparable. Stallions can form strong bonds and they never forget. In fact they can be much easier than mares.

"I bought Honeyman as a three year old and decided when he was ten years old I would like to breed from him. I bought a mare that I felt would compliment his bloodlines. She produced two colts - now two and four-year-olds. I sold Honeyman two years ago. His owners took him to another producer who wrapped him in cotton wool, put him in an isolation stable because he is a stallion, gave him no turnout and showed him too much. It was a big ask for a mature pony that's not used to that kind of regime. Honeyman ended up stressed and miserable. He started being naughty and his performance in the ring suffered as a result. His owners were at their wits end and they asked me to have him back. It was a relief to get him back here and I chucked him straight out on big field with his mates to recover. He then went back to winning again being shown and ridden by the owner's daughter.

94

"I lost a top quality stallion last year called Veary Nightfever. He was a prolific winner and was following in Honeyman's footsteps. He came in one day slightly unsound. The vets diagnosed an abscess in one foot. No one realised that he also had laminitis in that one foot as well. He wasn't fat and it is very unusual to get laminitis in only one foot. They treated for the abscess for ten days and then rushed him to Newmarket but it was too late. It was devastating and you never recover but at least I now have Honeyman's three quarter brother Moortown Statesman and Honeyman's sons to bring on.

Moortown Statesman

"Some very good news is that Honeyman recently retired to stud studies at the Springwater Stud in Devon. They have fifty-five acres for their ponies and are through and through Dartmoor enthusiasts. He such a super pony and I can't think of a better place for him to retire to."

Equine Veterinary Consultant
Helen Gibb
(BVetMed CertAVP (EM) MRCVS)

**Helen Gibb
with Connemara
Carraun Lord Arthur**

Helen is an advanced veterinary practitioner specialising in equine medicine. She graduated from the Royal Veterinary College, London in 2008. She has a particular interest in poor performance, respiratory disorders and reproduction. Helen has had a long association with British Native ponies. While at school she helped out at a Welsh pony stud in her summer holidays including getting yearlings ready for the sales. She also helped to back Shetlands at another stud. Her first pony was a grey Connemara called 'Rambler' whom she shared with her sister for eight years. Rambler taught both girls how to ride - and fall off! Helen enjoyed a variety of activities but Rambler's favourite 'thing' was gymkhana games, particularly Chase Me Charlie. Her second pony was a grey Welsh x Arab called 'Rupert' who was an absolute demon to show jump (mostly out of control!). She hacked him for miles and miles, getting up to all kinds of mischief. Unfortunately he was euthanised at eight years old with a rare lung tumour.

Helen currently owns an eight year old Cob x Warmblood called Pogo who is proving to be lots of fun. She has recently started to compete at British Dressage and hopes to affiliate for British Eventing this year.

Fair Laddie of Suffield

Photo Credits

All photos copyright Caroline Brett except:

19   Gue Jules and Gue Opal: *Carole Laignel*
41   Brandon Fiery Jack, Gue Handsome and Gue Kyle: *Carole Laignel*
45   Lunsdale Mountain Mist: *Gabriela Jasurkova*
48   Gue foals: *Carole Laignel*
49   Goldie of Gue: *Carole Laignel*
50   Kirkshall Achilles: *Tawna Stud*
51   Brandon Fiery Jack: *Carole Laignel*
52   Gue stallions and Gue youngsters: *Carole Laignel*
53   Moss-side Uilleam Mor: *Moss-side Stud*
54   Moss-side Domhnach: *Moss-side Stud*
55   Moss-side Iain Mor: *Julia Shearwood*
58   Moss-side Iain Mor: *Sian Broderick*
59   Swarfedale Prince Regent: Care of *Roandale stud*
60   Lowkbers Bracken: Care of *Roandale stud*
61   Roandales ponies: *Gina Parker*
62   LunesdalePonies: *Lunesdale Stud*
63   Lunesdale Tarquin and Lunesdale Warlord: Care of *Lunesdale Stud*
64   Lunsdale Mountain Mist: *Gabriela Jasurkova*
65   Lunesdale Henry: Care of *Lunesdale Stud*
67   Lunesdale Colts: *Lunesdale Stud*
68   Bunowen Castle Ri: *Pam Clingan FredTheCat.co.uk*
70   Bunowen Castle Ri: *Pam Clingan FredTheCat.co.uk*
71   Haselor Cormack: *Rebecca Penny*
72   Llanarth Prince of Wales: *Stephanie Fitt*
74   Llanarth Seldom Seen: *Charlotte Jenson*
75   Llanarth Prince of Wales: *ESPhotography*
76   Powys Sprite: *AGC Photography*
77   Blaenpentre Silver Coin: *The Event Photographer'*
79   Powys Sprite: *AGC Photograph*
81   Powys Sprite: *Christine Latter*
82   Knavesash Knight: *Tallauders*
83   Mallards Wood Goddess: *Tallauders*
100 Chippy: *Rosemary Brett*

About The Author

Caroline riding Chippy

Caroline learned to ride on Chippy, a New Forest pony, when she was four. Some years later when Chippy was retired, Caroline plagued her 'unhorsey' parents for lessons at a local riding school. Her favourite pony there was a cream dun Connemara. She spent many school holidays riding with a friend on Welsh ponies near Abergavenny and a Connemara in Yorkshire. Her first pony, bought with years of accumulated savings, was a cremello Welsh Section B gelding. The pair did well competing at local gymkhana events.

At eighteen, Caroline was introduced to Highland ponies by her godmother, Sally Coutts. Sally taught Caroline to break in Highlands to ride and drive, starting a lifelong passion for the breed. Although Caroline has owned various thoroughbreds to event, hunt and play polocrosse on, there's always been a Highland 'about the place'. She started breeding fourteen years ago and now has a stallion and three mares. She hacks, drives, shows and has recently started competing her Highlands successfully at Trec. The ponies are her pride and joy.